ALIGHT HERE

An Anthology of Falkirk Writing

Edited by Alan Bissett

Cargo Publishing

Alight Here
An anthology of Falkirk Writing
Edited by Alan Bissett
First Published by Cargo Publishing in 2015
SC376700
This collection © Falkirk Community Trust 2015
Registered charity no. SC042403
Each story © the individual author 2015

ISBN 978-1-910741-03-0

Printed & Bound in England by CPI
Cover design by Kaajal Modi
Illustration by Ottavia Pasta

www. cargopublishing. com

Also available as:
Kindle Ebook
EPUB Ebook

Supported by
The National Lottery®
through Creative Scotland

ALBA | CHRUTHACHAIL

creative place awards
winner 2014

Falkirk
**Community
Trust**

Contents

Foreword

Part One: NOW

Alan Bissett
'Falkirk? Oh, I've Passed Through it on the Train...'
An Introduction
David Victor
There was a Bairn went Forth
Brian McCabe
Botticelli's Flytrap
Claire Wilson
One Big Sunday in Falkirk
Peter Callaghan
Spring
In This Moment
Janet Paisley
Enough Rope
Helen MacKinven
Today's Special at the York Café
Samuel Best
Bruce's Taxis
Bethany Ruth Anderson
Day Trip
Constance Saim-Hunter
Homecomings
Lindsay Scott
Soutie
Lorna Fraser
Munitionette
Karyn Dougan
Aisle 10
Paul Cowan
Rab the Stab

Paul Tonner
    A Poem for Alan Davie
Dickson Telfer
    One Nil
Brian McNeill
    Flash Gorton's Leg
Matt Hamilton
    Eyelashes
Aidan Moffat
    A Beginner's Guide to Romance in the Falkirk District
Gordon Legge
    All She Was Worth
Gary Oberg
    Under Prospect Hill

Part Two: THEN

Alan Bissett
    'The Dear Auld Hame': An Introduction
Robert Burns
    Lines at Falkirk (1787)
    Lines at Carron (1787)
William Benson
    Reply to Robert Burns (1787)
Robert Keir
    Sweet Wood of Callendar (1827)
Robert Buchanan
    A New Year's Sang for Fa'kirk (1857)
    Address to Fa'kirk after the Celebration of Burns' Centenary
    (1859)
    Grangemouth Glories no. II (1864)
Anonymous
    Petition of Bo'ness Steeple to the Inhabitants (c. 1865)
James Black Cameron
    Dedicated to Miss Annie Russell, Falkirk (1877)

Anonymous
    School Song (1884)
Wallace Maxwell
    Lines on the Falkirk "Bairns" who fell at Tamai (c. 1897)
Charles James Finlayson
    The Lass o' Carron Side (c. 1897)
Anonymous
    The Highlandmen Came Down the Hill (c. 1897)
Mary Bowie Gillespie
    Carronside (c. 1897)
John A. Thomson
    Ae wintry nicht, when winds blaw snell (c. 1908)
    Amalgamation (c. 1908)
Corporal Dalling
    Camelon in the Shire (c. 1916)
Alexander Stewart
    Redding, 25th Sept 1923 (1923)
Anonymous
    Falkirk Fe'en Fair (c. 1925)
John Fleming
    Auld Fa'kirk Toon and its Bairns (c. 1928)
    An Address tae Auld Fa'kirk Steeple (1928)
James Brown
    Carron Glen (1932)
William Gordon
    The Braw Toon o' Grangemouth (1946)
    Go to Denny (1946)

Author Biographies

Acknowledgements

Foreword

In January 2014, Falkirk was designated a Creative Place following a successful bid to Creative Scotland's 2014 Creative Place Awards. The bid was coordinated by Falkirk Community Trust on behalf of a number of partner agencies (Falkirk Council Education Services, Falkirk Council Development Services, NHS Forth Valley Arts & Wellbeing project, Artlink Central, Forth Valley Open Studios, Falkirk & District Arts and Civic Council) based in the Falkirk area.

The Creative Place award has been an opportunity for us to develop targeted programmes of work that seek to complement and build on the distinctive features of cultural activity in the area. Using the broad theme of 'people, routes and pathways' we have put together three distinct projects that focus on engaging local audiences; engaging those passing through and engaging the rest of the world, respectively.

Developed in the Year of Homecoming, our Creative Place programme also provided an opportunity to welcome back locally-born artists to inspire and nurture a new generation of creative people. Within this context, we were delighted that author and playwright, Alan Bissett accepted our invitation to curate an anthology of writing that seeks to create a dialogue between the communities resident in the Falkirk area and the thousands of commuters who pass through every day by rail, road, cycle path or canal.

Alan has brought together new works by esteemed writers originally from the area with works from writers (emerging and established) currently based here, that have been selected through an open competition. He has also included poetry and prose drawn from the Falkirk archives – voices from past times that resonate with contemporary concerns.

It has been a pleasure to work with Alan on this project. He has brought tremendous energy, enthusiasm, imagination and insight to the Creative Place programme. In addition to working on the anthology, he was keen to develop and write a play for the area that could tour to community venues and schools. *What the F**kirk!* is a theatre experience for people who don't necessarily go to the theatre, and as with *Alight Here,* seeks to draw out something of the identity of the area through the words of those who reside in it or grew up there.

Alight Here and *What the F**kirk!* are fantastic endorsements of Falkirk's Creative Place award but they also point to an exciting future, where creativity in both its broadest and most specific sense is integral to the notion of 'the place to be'.

Paul Eames, Team Leader – Arts, Falkirk Community Trust

Falkirk
NOW

'Falkirk? Oh, I've Passed Through it on the Train…'

An Introduction

Alan Bissett

Oh to hell with it, I'm going to start off by doing the most un-Falkirk thing I could do right now: boast.

In 2008 I was awarded Falkirk Personality of the Year by the Arts and Civic Council. Beyond the town, whenever I mentioned this, I was greeted with almost universal chuckling ('There couldn't have been much of a shortlist!' 'Is that when they're going to give you a personality?') but I'd never felt prouder than I was then, being recognised by my hometown. I went along to the prize-giving ceremony at the Town Hall with a lightness of heart, only to sit through around two and half hours of awards being given, almost exclusively, to local sports clubs. This, from the *Arts* and Civic Council.

Obviously, I was very grateful for the award, and I've nothing against local sports clubs! It's much better that people involve themselves in physical activity than not, and it's right that their achievements should be rewarded by the local community. But *only* sport? Sport can be many wonderful things – and I'd direct people towards **Dickson Telfer**'s story 'One Nil' in this book, for a witty appraisal of football's place in Falkirk – but it is competitive first and foremost, the triumph of precision, strength and speed over imagination, creativity or free thought. I was alarmed by the lack of balance in the human qualities that Falkirk was choosing to 'officially' recognise at this awards ceremony and wondered what this said about the town, its self-perception, its perhaps innate conservatism. I remembered something that Falkirk bairns Aidan Moffat and Malcolm Middleton had said to me, after their band Arab Strap's packed New York gig in 2005: 'It's funny, but when we play in our home town no-one shows up…'

As Alasdair Gray writes about Glasgow, in his 1981 masterpiece novel *Lanark*:

> Nobody imagines living here…. Think of Florence, Paris, London, New York. Nobody visiting them for the first time is a stranger, because he's already visited them in paintings, novels, history books and films. But if a city hasn't been used by an artist not even the inhabitants live there imaginatively.

That people do now inhabit Glasgow 'imaginatively' is largely because of the sea-change brought about by *Lanark* itself, but we could equally apply Gray's statement to any place that is not considered an elite centre of culture.

Grangemouth's Alan Davie may have become a giant of Twentieth-Century Scottish painting, but in fiction Falkirk was fairly invisible until recent decades, with the prominence of three writers in the 1990s: Janet Paisley, Gordon Legge, Brian McCabe. It was only after I left Falkirk in my late teens, and started to consume Scottish literature, that I realised the national esteem in which these three were held. Paisley, from the Glen Village, had won awards for her play *Refuge* and her poetry was setting a new pace in Scots language writing; Legge, from Grangemouth, was a key figure in the 'Rebel Inc' generation that defined Scottish literature in the Nineties; and McCabe, who'd even been to the same school as me, Falkirk High, was considered simply one of the finest short-story writers in the country. If *they* were from Falkirk and *they* could do it, I thought, then so could I. The influence of example. I was not alone.

Between them they caused a late, literary blooming in Falkirk, giving younger writers the confidence to create work about their own people or using their own language, of which this anthology is merely one effect.

Of course, this renewal isn't just limited to literature. The aforementioned band Arab Strap have been hugely influential, way beyond these shores, but their early gigs were in Pennies and Changes, the club round the back of Coasters roller-rink in the Boag, and Moffat and Middleton still refuse to dilute their Falkirk accents when they sing. Guitarist and songwriter Adam Stafford was not only shortlisted for Scottish Album of the Year in 2013 but directed a 2009 short film about the Grangemouth Oil Refinery explosion, 'The Shutdown', which won a plethora of awards at international film festivals. The Cocteau Twins, from Grangemouth itself, produced an ethereal, shimmering electronica which set them apart from any other kind of music being made on the planet. Then of course there's multi-instrumentalist, Bill Wells.

None of these artists produce safe, comfortable, couthy 'tourist tat', but challenging, uncompromising and soulful works of art. Falkirk can be avant-garde and edgy as much as it can be familiar and conservative, as proven by **Paul Tonner**'s experimental 'Poem for Alan Davie' in this collection, an exhilarating attempt by a Falkirk artist to make art about the art of a Falkirk artist!

So what is Falkirk? Is it an unremarkable, post-industrial town, much like others in Scotland: Dunfermline, Elgin, or Paisley? Maybe the behaviour and beliefs of people here are the same as those in places of Falkirk's size all over the world. Perhaps it is a Caledonian version of Springfield from *The Simpsons*, or one of those refinery-towns you might find in a Bruce Springsteen album, characterised only by its averageness.

Or is Falkirk unique, with its own history, dialect, landscape, architecture and culture, all of which adds up to a distinct accent of the mind?

This book is partly an attempt to answer that question. Including poetry, fiction and memoir from writers who have some meaningful connection with the town – because they were either born or moved here – it presents a place that is both average *and* distinct. The emotional travails of the characters in these pages may be universal, but they take place against a visual backdrop that could be nowhere else but Falkirk – its particular schools, parks, pubs and workplaces – often using a voice that is rich with local flavour.

So we might ask: what *does* make Falkirk different? Most people – receiving their cultural agenda from Hollywood, Netflix or the BBC – are now alienated from a sense of their own history. Far from being a nowhere town in which nothing happens, Falkirk has actually been at the crux of events at every stage of Scottish history. Even before

Scotland was formed, the Antonine Wall, scars from which remain in the ground at Callendar Park, represented the very edges of the Roman Empire. William Wallace lost to King Edward, Hammer of the Scots, at the first Battle of Falkirk in 1298. The marriage contract between Mary Queen of Scots and Francis II of France was signed in Callendar House in 1558. From the late 18th Century, the town was host to one of the largest cattle markets in Europe. The Jacobites defeated the British Crown forces during the Battle of Falkirk Muir in 1746. And the town was, of course, the centre of the industrial revolution in Scotland, a manufacturing miracle which produced much of the coal, steel, iron and brick which powered the British Empire.

It is this Falkirk about which **Lorna Fraser** writes in 'Munitionette'. Her story about the female labourers who supplied shells from the iron works in World War I resounds with both detail and atmosphere. This history also inspires **Lindsay Scott**'s 'Soutie', which looks at the brutal experience of imperialism. The moment when his narrator finds a cast-iron cooking-pot from Carron as far away as Angola shows both the extent to which Falkirk's industrial achievements were widespread and the town's unfortunate complicity in colonialism.

Despite the demise of much of Falkirk's heavy industry, its self-image as a working-class town, where men sweat, toil and engage in cruel, often hilarious banter, has not diminished. **Brian McCabe**'s 'Botticelli's Flytrap' and **Paul Cowan**'s 'Rab the Stab' showcase the wisdom, wit and ribald concerns of the ordinary worker, beneath the looming shadow of the Grangemouth Oil Refinery or the Smith & Wellstood factory in Bonnybridge.

There is, however, a gentler side to Falkirk. An industrial powerhouse it may have been, but at every stage machinery fought with nature for dominance of the town. The rural and the urban lie side by side here, the pastoral and modernity intertwining to curious effect. After all, Callendar Woods blooms in the imagination just as easily as Carron Iron Works. This is why **Peter Callaghan**'s beautiful nature poems – 'Spring' and 'In This Moment' – feel just as congruent in this collection as the busier cut-and-thrust of McCabe and Cowan's labourers.

Of course, as anyone who grew up here understands, your own 'bit' of Falkirk is as important, if not more so, than 'Falkirk' itself, which is a name often just used to refer to the town centre. People who come from Camelon, Denny, Laurieston, Langlees, Polmont, Shieldhill or Tamfourhill take pride in that fact, since each of these villages or schemes has their own distinct identity which might make sense only to someone who lives there. Such places often define themselves against their neighbouring villages, which can lead to rivalries both friendly and unfriendly.

How many times can you fold a piece of paper? I grew up in Hallglen, and within that sealed world – enclosed by Callendar Woods to the north and the Union Canal to the south – we described ourselves as being from 'Phase 1', 'Phase 2', 'Phase 3' or 'Phase 6' (what became of Phases 4 and 5 is shrouded in mystery). No-one outside of Hallglen could be expected to understand what these territories were, or even where they began and ended, but anyone who lived there knew exactly what was implied when someone said, 'Dinnay mess wi him, he's Phase 3!' Given that Hallglen, built as recently as 1975, had a modern Lego bricks aesthetic, accommodated a large amount of Glasgow overspill, which most likely contributed to the accent, featured an arcane system of streets and underpasses which baffled visitors, we can see that it is a very different place, from, say, the ancient Glen Village, which is right next to it, Bonnybridge, with its UFO legends, or Slamannan, with its mining and farming heritage.

My mother's family, indeed, hail from Slamannan, and whenever they are drunk they still sing the Slamannan songs passed down to them when they were children and which contain the characters and landmarks of yesteryear. Every area of Falkirk probably has, or certainly *had*, such songs, lore, ghost tales, urban legends and eccentricities which give it colour and continuity with the past. This is my hope, at least. I wonder if the onward march of technology and consumerism is eroding that sense of native culture. It's why I delighted in **Gary Oberg**'s story 'Prospect Hill', which melds local myth to landscape and ends up with a ghost/love story that could only come from the pen of a Bairn.

This theme is something which comes up frequently among the work in this book: the feeling that the past is becoming ever-more intangible, lost to a corporate colonisation which makes Falkirk High Street – with its McDonalds, Greggs and WH Smiths – seem pretty much exactly like every other across the UK. At the junction of Manor Street and Kirk Wynd, for example, are two coffee shops, directly across from each other. One is small, charming and locally-owned, the other is Costa. When I walk past them I can see that, more often than not, customers choose the faceless brand-name – whose profits end up with the Whitbread corporation – over support for a Falkirk enterprise.

For such reasons, numerous shops and businesses which give the town its own character and economy have suffered over the last few decades. **Helen MacKinven**'s mournful 'Today's Special at the York Café' illustrates this point, while **Samuel Best**'s sharp and ambiguous 'Bruce's Taxis' features a pair of boys on their way to City nightclub who wrestle with the legacy of Falkirk's past.

There is also sense in a few of these works that 'community', a most human and necessary thing for which places like Falkirk were once valued, has been eroded by governments who've fostered our most selfish and competitive instincts at the expense of empathy and kindness. This introduction is not a forum for politics, but it's certainly the case that fences between neighbours have grown higher since the 1980s. Each village in Falkirk used to have an annual Gala Day, where the people of Redding, Bainsford, Carronshore or Maddiston would come together and celebrate their community. These are few and far between now. It's good to see **Claire Wilson** bringing this spirit back, along with their bonhomie and humour, in her story 'One Big Sunday in Falkirk'.

A sense of community and fairness has not left our writers, who in many ways preserve Falkirk's morality and soul. This is why powerful stories here such as **Janet Paisley**'s 'Enough Rope' and **Brian McNeill**'s 'Flash Gorton's Leg' stand up for those struggling at the bottom of the social ladder against the cruel offices of state who want to pull that ladder up.

A feeling of nostalgia for a lost Falkirk finds expression too in writing about childhood. **Aidan Moffat** (of Arab Strap fame) offers 'A Beginner's Guide to Romance in the Falkirk District', as boyish passions are recounted using many voices and devices, at least one of which is distinctly Falkirk's. **David Victor**'s poem 'There Was a Bairn Went Forth' follows a young man from childhood larks in the Mariner Centre to the darker, more complex world of adulthood, using Falkirk scenery as a lens through which to examine this maturing.

Victor's Whitman-esque theme of a soul heading out into the world from humble beginnings finds echo in stories about Bairns returning to the town after a pronlonged absence. Falkirk is the sort of place that people often leave – to go to university or find work – and come back to later in life to raise children, be close to ailing parents, or simply remember who they once were. **Constance Saim-Hunter** exemplifies this in her evocative memoir 'Homecoming', as she sees Falkirk change, over a span of decades, with each new homewards journey she makes. **Bethany Anderson**'s 'Day Trip' is spikier and more ambivalent: a student attempts to prove to her patronising flatmate that Falkirk is not simply a scrounger's paradise, only to discover a complex cocktail within herself of guilt, loss, pride and relief at having left. Anyone who has ever 'come home' to anywhere will recognise these feelings. You might think you're done with Falkirk, as the saying goes, but Falkirk is never done with you.

Most of these stories and poems reflect something unique about Central Scotland – whether environmental, linguistic or cultural – but there are some here which have no connection to the region other than the fact that they were written by someone born here. **Gordon Legge**'s 'All She Was Worth' is a fizzy romp through a life-long friendship which has developed from dark beginnings into Hollywood triumph. **Karyn Dougan**'s 'Aisle 10' starts out like chick-lit, before becoming a scalpel-sharp focus on the insecurities women have about themselves. **Matt Hamilton**'s chilling 'Eyelashes' is a quasi-Horror story about psychosis and... counting. None of these make any reference to Falkirk, which shows that our writers are still capable of looking out towards the world or in towards the psychological, without feeling the need to be defined by the place from which they come.

Falkirk is no longer invisible, to others or to ourselves. For so long we were used to telling people where we were from, only to hear them reply, 'Falkirk? Oh, I've passed through it on the train...' Now, all of a sudden, we are a tourist destination. The engineering miracle of the Falkirk Wheel and the breathtaking sculpture of the Kelpies have become national symbols. Artistic events are keeping pace with these developments. The live music scene is one of the few ways in which the town centre is improving. The National Theatre of Scotland devised a piece about the changing face of Falkirk's nightlife in 2012 called *Reasons to Dance*, which was performed in City nightclub. The *[Untitled]* literary magazine, the *Funny in Falkirk* comedy festival, and the *For Falkirk's Sake* and *Nomenclature* spoken word gigs have reinvigorated audiences and performers at the grassroots level. The Creative Scotland 'Creative Place' award to Falkirk is recognition of all these things and more. This anthology is just one facet of that windfall which will hopefully inspire future writers from Falkirk to generate their own sense of self.

No longer do Bairns have to get on the train to Glasgow or Edinburgh to discover culture. They can make it and consume it for themselves right here. And to those city-dwellers who only pass through at Falkirk High Station or Grahamston, we say, 'Alight here.'

There Was a Bairn Went Forth

David Victor

There was a Bairn went forth every day, though he came in cold, carved in Cumbernauld: what's it called, what's it called, what's it called?

And he wasn't even born there, cast out first from Tarbet, on the banks of that Loch, the one always echoed on the tablet boxes and shortbread tins.

Then he filtered in to the Kirk, familiar but foreign, with a Weegie accent that didnae ken,

And he was nae Bairn in Bantaskin, but he became the orange flats and the poplar trees and the grotesque graffiti of primary knobs and tip-ex titties,

Then he became fitba and skimming the grass, he could see the pass, and make the team,

And he became school-canteen-donkey-dick-hot-dogs, and pretended he couldn't do Maths and became the hideous taste of plasticine,

And became biking down roads, through Camelon (NOT Ca-me-lon), became the filth of the canal, the gentrification of the distillery, the fat-fermented stench of the Copper Top, a ten bob bag from Lemetti's.

And he became the reek of the Mariner Centre, reliving the A-Team and Baywatch in fake waves of chlorine and piss.

And the Bairn became lost in himself, in realising we're just waiting to die; in realising he knew nothing, till fresh blonde, nameless girls and skin like tenderness,

And he became almost crying when she wouldn't speak, because she was playing a game her parents played.

And Saturday mornings, he became pretending American, at the Superbowl by the Levi factory, Show me Heaven, ignoring her, by spending the money on Final Fight, with his mate, to prove he wasn't gay, in the old, ironic, heterosexual way. But then he became her lingering Chupa-Chup kiss and was never free, nor could ever listen to Maria McKee.

Then he became Falkirk High – rebuilt before the rebuild – consuming Camelon High, and he realised he could never become Tamfourhill, Hallglen, Camelon, Bantaskin – but became a posh twat coz he could read and wouldn't fail to succeed.

And he became his head down, he had to hide, because you can't let out what's burning inside, and he was a Negative Creep, In Bloom, he liked to sing along, to all the pretty songs.

Then he became the dull capitalist pilgrimage to the Howgate's bloated show, and complied rebelliously by stealing posters from Athena, and double-tapes from Our Price, that were disembowelled, left dangling like a mute web, then into the desperation of In-Shops.

And then HMV ate Sleeves.

And he became the drifting smoke of the underpass, and then Callendar Park and lost in lust amidst the trees, her hair and limbs and Charlie Red and the distant smudge of a memory.

Then he became the sandstone of the public library, and the mouldy damp warmth, and something familiar yet foreign, hidden in voices, in Whitman and Heaney and Duffy and Mahon.

And he became the dense daze of soft black and Teardrop and Standard Grades and Supergrass. Then he became scripted to suit situations, became lines retorted from a faint adaptation, sound bitten to avoid committing.

Then he became Brockville, he became Stainrod, Cadette, Eddie May, became the lies about games attended, matches memorised, became mob mentality and guttural gestures, became a bottle of Buckie in the Choir, became Tony Parks behind the ball, Tony Parks in Behind the Wall.

And boking at Fast Freddy's and then in the damp of Manse Place, fumbling her tight jeans, to see what anything means.

Then he had to leave, for all he'd known was foreign yet familiar. This all became part of the Bairn who went forth every day, a Bairn who couldn't stay, but who'll never, truly, be away.

Botticelli's Flytrap

Brian McCabe

I'd only been working at Smith & Wellstood for a week, on the night shift, but every night there came a point during the shift when I could sense it out there – the darkness and silence surrounding us. Everybody else in Bonnybridge was asleep, but in here, under the strip-lights, we were making industrial ceiling tiles through the night. It was a lonely feeling, but it was a shared loneliness.

I sat on a stack of wooden pallets in a dark corner of the factory floor, doing nothing except dreaming about who I might be in the future and what I might do – rock star, artist, writer? The fantasies weren't painless – Christine always came into them somehow. If I was on stage, she was in the audience, or waiting backstage, but she was never my fan. Even in my fantasies she was critical of my performance and making her own demands. If I was an artist or a writer – and with two As in Art and English from Falkirk High, I could surely be both if I put my mind to it – she might qualify as a model or a muse, but I knew her too well to think that she'd be flattered by some daubs on a canvas, or something called 'Love Poem'. Maybe that was why I liked her.

We'd split up during my first year at uni. Now she'd finished school as well and was working for the summer in a hotel in the Highlands. I couldn't imagine her doing kitchen work. It didn't fit my idea of her – someone almost mythically beautiful.

Work seemed to have ground to a halt, maybe because we'd run out of some material that couldn't be unloaded till the day shift came on. I had no idea why and didn't feel like asking. If I did, somebody might give me something to do, like cleaning the Riddle – the huge machine that punched all the holes in the sheet metal before it was guillotined and shaped into ceiling tiles. I was dead scared of the riddle. Operating it was like walking up and down inside the guts of a huge engine, the engine of a ship maybe, with these narrow walkways between the pistons and the wheels and the blades. Most of the safety guards were broken or loose or missing altogether. Sometimes Rab –

the apprentice who worked alongside me – poked fun at my caution. I was always for stopping the machine when we had to remove 'slugs' – bits of stuff that got on to the sheet metal sometimes and made dents in the tiles. He could poke fun all he wanted. I still wasn't sure what I wanted to be, but I knew I didn't want to be an industrial ceiling tile.

Nearby, at the work bench they used for their piece-time, three of the men were playing cards. Beside me, on a heap of old rags, Rab slept or pretended to, curled up under an oil-stained blanket, his boots sticking out one end and his black, close-cropped hair out the other. I opened my haversack. Between my piece-box and my flask, both empty now, was *The Story of Art*. I tugged the book out and lowered the haversack to the floor. I'd failed the first year exam in the History of Art. I had to pass the re-sit or I'd be out on my ear.

I opened the book and looked at some of the pictures, trying to memorise names and dates. Rab suffered from asthma – he'd failed the medical for the army – and every so often the rasp of his breathing distracted me. Either that or it was the shouts of the men playing cards. The factory lighting wasn't good for reading, and sometimes the print blurred and seemed to move around on the page. I found myself staring at Botticelli's Venus again. She didn't really look like Christine, but somehow she reminded me of her. Maybe it was her expression or the look in her eyes – but no, it was something I couldn't pin down. The picture filled me with a kind of hopeless longing.

I looked up when I heard the men cheering and clapping. Sammy, the gatehouse attendant, had come in with the wage packets. He carried them in what looked like a shoe box, and he'd put the box down on the work bench to clean his glasses with his hanky. I shook Rab's shoulder and told him our wages had arrived. He sat up and pretended to be waking from a deep sleep, stretching and yawning. I shut the book, jumped down from the pallets and walked over to the work bench where the men were. Rab followed me.

'Here comes Brian and his Gang,' said Archie McGlone, grinning. Every time he grinned he exposed the gap between his eye teeth where he'd taken his dental plate out. A lot of the men seemed to work without their teeth in on the night shift. Was it just because they were used to taking them out at night, or because there were no women on?

It was a question.

Mick McIver was the same, except with him it was the complete set of falsers, top and bottom. He kept them wrapped in a dirty rag in his boiler-suit pocket.

'Yous two are no getting peyd,' he said. 'Ye're too fuckin lazy.'

'Listen tae whae's talkin,' said Sammy. 'McIver the skiver.'

McIver's laughter was a harsh bark of derision, then he spat out: 'Fuck off ya miserable four-eyed cunt ye. Every time Ah pass that gatehouse ye've got the feet up, daein the fuckin crossword!'

'Aye, either that or he's studyin page three!' said Archie McGlone, working his eyebrows up and down, grinning and making his eyes dart from one side to the other. He looked like a ventriloquist's dummy.

'Aye, that'll be right,' said Sammy, then he shook his head, looked at me and Rab and blew some air out of his mouth in a display of disgust.

I got the feeling that this banter was for my benefit.

Sammy put his glasses on squintly, picked up the shoe box and sorted through the pay packets importantly.

I put *The Story of Art* face down on the work bench and sat on a metal crate. I shifted along a bit, reluctantly, to make room for Rab.

Since I'd come to the factory, Rab had latched on to me. He followed me around, sat beside me at piece-time, and usually ended up working with me. Maybe it was because I was the only other guy under twenty. At first I'd felt glad o the company. Then I'd felt sorry for him – most of the men seemed to treat him with contempt, or pity. Now I was beginning to feel impatient with his loyalty and wanted to shake him off.

'Awright boys?' said Jake Dunnigan, then he licked the paper of the cigarette he was rolling with exaggerated care. He was a lean, handsome man who always carried a comb in the back pocket of his jeans. His hair was slicked back and the collar of his donkey jacket was usually turned up. He was very much in charge of himself.

Mick shuffled the cards, nodded at me and Rab and said: 'Look at the paira them. Tweedle-fuckin-dee an Tweedle-fuckin-dum!'

Jake raised his eyebrow, lit up and half-closed his eyes in a show of mild amusement. He didn't let himself laugh very often. He was very controlled, but he gave me the feeling that if he ever lost control, chances are he wouldn't find it again until it was time to plead guilty.

His face was pale, pinched. His lips were thin, tight. If you asked him for the time, he'd look you in the eye very seriously before glancing at his watch and telling you. It was like you'd asked him something deeply personal.

McIver was different. He was liable to boil over at the least wee thing. Some of the men in the machine shop called him Mad Mick. On my first night, Archie McGlone had warned me about him. He'd called him a cowboy, a chancer, a heidbanger. I'd expected a young guy, but he was in his late fifties. In a way that added an edge to the reputation – he was still wild. He wore a dirty old mud-coloured polo-neck under his boiler-suit. His skin was leathery, as if he'd worked outside a lot. He probably had. He had a pug nose and sleekit-looking green eyes. He'd done some amateur boxing when he was younger. I'd heard he was still doing it – but not in the ring.

'Righto boys,' said Sammy. 'The moment yous have aw been waiting for.'

'No hauf, ' said Archie McGlone.

'Get on wi it, ya bumptious wee nyaff ye,' said Mick McIver.

Sammy rounded his eyes in outrage at this latest insult, then called out our names briskly as he threw us our wage packets. The men opened them, took out the pay-slips and studied them. I did the same. It was my first wage packet, and I couldn't help smiling with real pleasure when I saw the folded notes inside. I hadn't held so much cash in my hand for a long time.

When Sammy had gone, Mick leered at Jake, hammered the side of his fist on the work bench, held out his wage packet, shook it up and down and declared: 'Get a ride the night, eh?'

Archie McGlone grinned and said: 'Ah get yin anywey.'

'Aw? Lucky cunt you. Ah suppose she's lyin there waitin for ye every morning wi the suspenders on, is she?'

'Oh aye, definitely, that's right!'

Archie was grinning and rubbing his hands together furiously.

'Ye're a fuckin liar McGlone. Ah bet ye're lucky if she puts the kettle on for ye.'

'Wid ye listen tae yersels,' said Jake. 'Should be ashamed o yersels talkin like that in front o these young boys.'

'Away ye go,' said Mick. 'This yin's probly getting it every night up at the uni. That yin's too saft in the heid tae ken whit we're on aboot!'

'Ah might be saft in the heid, but that's no what coonts,' said Rab.

'Stoap that, ya rajie wee bastard ye,' said Jake, then he looked down at my lap and added, 'An you mind an keep yon thing in yer troosers up at the uni.'

I smiled uneasily. Since the split with Christine, my first year had passed without any chance to take it out. I wasn't making contact in other ways as well. One of my tutors had put his finger on it when he'd said to me: 'If you don't want to come to classes, that's up to you, but for heaven's sake *have a good time!*' I wasn't doing either. I wasn't fitting in. I felt intimidated by some of the other students, who seemed to know so much about Art already. It was like I was in a foreign country and didn't speak the language.

Mick shuffled the cards, slammed them on the table and took a half bottle of whisky from somewhere inside his boiler-suit. He unscrewed the cap, took a swig, then offered it to Jake. Jake looked over his shoulder to the door into the machine shop, then wiped the bottle and took a drink. Archie McGlone said he couldn't trust himself to take a drink at this time of the night. Mick laughed at this derisively. Rab wasn't even considered. He offered the bottle to me.

I didn't want the drink, but I didn't want to turn it down either. I took it and tried to look like I'd done this before, but the whisky made me wince. Archie and Mick roared with laughter. Mick thumped me on the back as he took the bottle out of my hand. He had another swig, drinking so much that his Adam's apple moved up and down in his throat. He smacked his lips and rolled his toothless jaws around, his eyes narrowing like a cat's, then he tucked the bottle back into his boiler-suit and said:

'Gie ye a tip, son – see whisky? Sometimes when ye've been drinkin whisky, ye can ride aw night. Ither times ye cannae even get it up – that right, Jake?'

Jake, who was humming a tune to himself and smoking with a preoccupied air, glanced at me and said:

'Aye, that's yin o life's great mysteries, right enough.'

'Take the pish if ye like, ' said Mick. 'Fuckin true though.'

Archie McGlone offered me his tuppence-worth:

'Dinnae listen tae him. You get yersel a guid wee wife, son. She'll look efter ye. If ye feel like a bitty the ither, ye dinnae have tae gawn oot lookin for it. Ye juist gawn ben the room. If ye feel like a bevvy, ye can ayewis huv a few cans put by in the fridge.'

'Aye, an ye can even ask her fuckin permission tae drink yin, ' said Mick, cowering and clasping his hands together in a parody of the henpecked husband begging for a can of beer. Jake almost laughed. But it wasn't real. It was like somebody saying: I am laughing. I think that is funny.' Mick was watching Jake closely. He sniffed up his phlegm, stood up, put his pay packet in his pocket and announced: 'Ah'm away for a pish.'

When Mick had gone, Jake turned over *The Story of Art* and opened it. He flicked through the pages casually, tilting his head a little as he looked at the pictures. The book happened to fall open at the picture I'd looked at most.

'Whit d'ye cry this yin?'

'Eh... that's Botticelli's Venus.'

'Nice wee paira tits on her.'

Archie threw his head back and gave out a gargling laugh. Jake turned his head in Archie's direction very slowly and gave him a withering look. The gesture seemed to take ages. He opened his mouth, then he spoke:

'What the fuck's funny, McGlone? Ah suppose you're the tits expert round here.'

'Aye,' said McGlone, 'Ah've seen better in *Playboy*.'

'Ye mean bigger, is that what ye mean?'

'Aye. The bigger the better, eh boys?'

Rab dug me in the ribs with his elbow and laughed a low laugh. I didn't join in. He was really bothering me.

'Shows how much you ken aboot Art,' said Jake. He flicked through the book and stopped to look at another picture. He raised an eyebrow and gave a low whistle. Archie leaned over to look.

They had their heads together, these grown men, to look at the masterpiece, as if it was a rare kind of pornography they hadn't come across before.

Jake turned the picture to me and said: 'What's this yin cried?'

It was one of the paintings I'd failed to identify in the exam, and I still couldn't. If I was put in a corner, I'd probably have plumped for a title like 'The Rape of Lucretia'.

'I think it's a Titian.'

'The tits are nothin tae write hame aboot. Some arse on her though, eh?'

'Aye, that's mair like it, ' said Archie, nodding and grinning. 'Ah wouldnae kick her oot o bed.'

Jake looked at me and winked.

'Away ye go McGlone, she'd eat ye for breakfast, eh boys?'

'She can hae me for breakfast any day,' said Rab.

Jake left it to Archie to tell me to tell Rab to shut up.

Mick came back in buttoning up his boiler-suit and whistling. When he came up to the work bench, he leaned over Jake's shoulder to look at the book.

'Whit's this – pornography?'

'Naw, it's Art, ' said Archie. 'Here Mick, which yin dae you fancy, the tits-yin or the botty-what's-it?'

Jake flicked through the pages to find the Botticelli. When he did, Rab stuck his head in front of the picture and said: 'Reminds me o that wee burd in the paint shop. Sandra something.'

Archie looked at Rab askance.

'Sandra Purves? You have got tae be jokin! Some Venus her, eh?'

'Aye,' said Mick. 'A fuckin Venus flytrap!'

Rab grinned sheepishly as the men laughed at him.

Mick looked at Botticelli's Venus briefly and said: 'Naw. Ah've met her type. Fuckin prick-teaser. Let's see the ither yin again.'

Jake turned the pages to the Titian, if it was a Titian.

'She's the yin for me,' said Mick. 'Ah like a bitty meat.'

'Tellt ye,' said Archie to Jake.

Jake shook his head at the others' lack of taste and said: 'It's the tits we're talkin aboot. Which yin's got the nicer paira tits?'

Mick sat down, spat in his hands and rubbed them together. His tongue wriggled between his toothless gums, his eyes narrowed, then he said: 'It's no the tits ye ride.'

Jake agreed with this very seriously, as if Mick had made a very profound point. Archie grinned, then the grin soured on his face and he nodded and said: 'Aye, right enough.'

Jake went on looking at pictures. After a minute, Archie said: 'Put that book away afore Ah get too excited.'

'Ye've probably got a hard-on already McGlone, ' said Mick.

'So? What if Ah dae?'

'It's no meant tae gie ye a hard-on. It's Art, eh?'

He looked at me for confirmation. I shrugged and nodded.

Jake went on flicking through the pages, stopping to study a nude every so often. At one point Mick grabbed the book from him and pointed at a photograph of a Greek statue of the god Mars.

'How come they've aw got totty wee wullies?'

I didn't know. It wasn't a question that had come up in any of the tutorials I'd got to.

'Must've been an awfy cauld morning, ' said Archie, then he gargled on his own laughter loudly.

'Ye should ask yer fuckin teacher, ' said Mick, throwing the book on the work bench with contempt.

'Heh. Watch the boy's book, eh?' said Jake. He turned the book over and opened it respectfully.

'Ah used tae draw a bit masel, but Ah didnae hae the talent. This cousin o mine, Eddie, he had it. He could look at that picter an draw that Venus, the exact same thing, perfect. Frae memory tae. Telln ye. He could dae thon whit-d'ye-cry-it. Laughin Cavalier – is that yin in here?'

I shook my head and said I didn't think so.

Jake looked disappointed. He took a long draw on his cigarette, blew the smoke out like a sigh, then looked at me very seriously and said: 'You stick in, son. You learn aboot Art an that. Learn yersel a foreign language – Italian, French, Spanish an that. Then ye can fuck off away frae this dump. No like us. We're fuckin stuck here.'

Mick was shuffling the cards impatiently.

'Ach stoap putting ideas in the boy's heid, ya daft cunt ye.'

Jake clenched his jaws and looked at Mick steadily.

'Who're you callin a cunt?'

'If ye think the boy's gonnae be better off ower there, in Italy or Spain or some fuckin place, ye must be a daft cunt. It's the fuckin same everywhere. Them an us. As for learnin aboot Art – what the fuck use if that gonnae be tae him? Whit kinda joab's he gonnae get wi a degree in aw that fuckin stuff? Answer me that.

But Jake decided Mick wasn't worth answering. He said to me:

'Dinnae listen tae that ignorant bastard.'

Before he could say any more, Mick flung the pack of cards on the work bench so violently that they scattered everywhere. He was up on his feet and stabbing the air with a finger and shouting: 'Call me an ignorant bastard, wid ye? It's yersel ye're talkin aboot ya cunt ye. Art, by fuck – try tellin us aboot Art? You donno fuck-all aboot it Dunnigan so don't fuckin come it!'

Jake's face was pale, his mouth tight, his knuckles white. Without taking his eyes off Mick, he began to rise from his seat slowly. Suddenly Archie was on his feet, one hand on Jake's shoulder, the other held up to Mick, his grin now a grimace of fear. He danced around frantically between them.

'Aw c'mon now boys, cool it! This isnae the time or the place… We're no gonnae fight ower a fuckin Art book, c'mon now, dinnae be silly—'

He went on saying things like that, all the time gesticulating and pulling faces, until Mick sat down again, then Jake did the same.

Archie tried to make a joke of it all as he gathered the scattered cards together: 'See aw the trouble ye've caused? Ye come in here frae yer Edinburry University wi yer fancy books on Art an yer big ideas an see whit happens—'

Mick snatched the cards from Archie's hands and began to shuffle them.

'Aw shut it McGlone,' he said.

'Aye, button it,' said Jake.

Rab dug me in the ribs with his elbow, rolled his eyes and let out a low, soft whistle.

'Right,' said Mick. 'Put the fuckin art gallery away an let's have a game. Fancy a wee game o pontoons, boys?'

'Coont me oot,' said Rab.

'Surprise surprise. Whit aboot you, Brian?'

I shrugged and nodded. It was the first time Mick had called me by my name, and I felt pleased.

Mick dealt the cards. It felt good to take the money out of my wage packet and toss it into the kitty with an air of contempt like the others. Rab was my supporter, and every so often he'd blow on one of the cards I was given for luck. More often than not, this seemed to bring the card bad luck, and after a while I stopped him doing it. Then looked so sad that I relented and let him blow on a card. If I won, he cheered. When I lost, he commiserated with me. It didn't matter if I won or I lost. I was playing, that was what mattered.

Conversation dwindled, and time seemed to congeal around the card game. I was drawn into the repetition and the boredom of it – it was a new kind of boredom for me, and it was irresistible.

Later, I sat with Rab on the prongs of a fork-lift, drinking tea from paper cups. Rab had gone to the tea machine and brought them back for us. I had opened he book and was turning the pages, but Rab didn't seem to take the hint.

'How much did he skin ye?'

'Not much. A few quid.'

'See when Jake Dunnigan started getting up – Christ! Ah wis like that.' He held out his hand and made it shake. 'Ah wis sure they were gonnae thump the shit ootae each other. Were you no?'

I shrugged and drank some tea. Rab shook his head, imagining what had almost taken place between Mick and Jake. After a moment, he went on: 'Aw because o yon book! They nude picters! Fuckin mental, so it is!'

'Yeh, mental.'

There was a long silence between us. I turned a few pages and stopped again at Botticelli's Venus. It still made me think of Christine, except now Jake and Mick's voices were getting in the way: *Nice wee paira tits on her. Fuckin prick-teaser.*

Rab finished his tea, then crunched up the cup in his hand, threw it on the floor and stamped on it with his boot. Suddenly he looked at me and asked: 'You winchin, or what?'

I shook my head and sent the question back to him. Rab nodded and beamed, hardly able to contain his pride.

'We're getting engaged.'

'Is that right? When?'

'Soon as Ah've saved up enough for the ring.'

'Congratulations, Rab. Nice, is she?'

'Aye. Better lookin than her any day.'

A dismissive nod at Botticelli's Venus.

When he asked me if there was nobody I even fancied, I told him about the split with Christine. When I'd finished, he asked: 'Still love her, dae ye?'

I shrugged, opened my mouth to answer but couldn't. Rab was watching me closely, and he came to my rescue: 'Mibbe yez'll get back thegither then.'

I wanted to be on my own to think about that. I shut the book, finished my tea, then told Rab I was going for a smoke and walked to the back door of the factory.

Outside, I leaned against the factory wall and smoked. A train sped by – the overnight train from London, heading north. I tried to fantasise about Christine: those wondering blue eyes, that coppery red hair of hers, her lips parting in the prelude to a smile... It was the same picture I'd often painted in my mind, but now it seemed different. I realised it had become a memory.

I looked at the huddle of houses on the other side of the reservoir, in High Bonnybridge. One of those houses was mine, my mum and my dad were sleeping there. It was my home. It was where I was from. I tried to make it out, but it was still too dark. If I waited a bit longer, until it was light, maybe then I'd be able to see it.

One Big Sunday in Falkirk

Claire Wilson

Sunday 28th May 2000

'It's a fantastic opportunity for the people of Falkirk, you know, it shows that big events can happen outside of Glasgow and Edinburgh...'

'That was Brandon Bruce, organiser of Big in Falkirk, which is due to kick off later this afternoon in Callendar Park...'

I switched off the radio and yawned. I had been waiting for this day since March and it was finally here. I jumped out of bed and tentatively peered out of the curtains.

'Please don't be raining, please don't be raining,' I muttered to myself. The weather was cloudy but dry. However, it was only 7am. As long as it didn't turn wet or windy then I would be happy. I had an important task to achieve and I had to look my best.

My best friend Denise and I were catching the 9am bus into town and I had to be at her house in just over an hour and a half. I was so full of nervous energy that I could easily have walked the three miles from my home to the park.

The 'mini music festival' wasn't due to start until 1pm but I was desperate to be the first person there so I could be in the front row. It was imperative that Craig David would see me and ask for my phone number.

I had been to see Boyzone at the SECC a few months before and I was so far from the stage that I'd had to use binoculars to be able to see them. Literally.

I removed all the revision books from my desk and replaced them with all the makeup I owned and the outfit I planned to wear that I had carefully selected the previous day. With only two Standard Grade exams left to sit, I was glad of a day off from studying. The SQA had left the two worst subjects to last, Maths and Geography. I was poor at both.

I put on my *Huge Hits 99* CD to get me in the mood. I swayed in time to Craig David's vocals in front of my mirror.

'Once I marry Craig David I won't need to worry about school or exams anymore and all my friends will be super jealous,' I informed my reflection.

I turned on the shower, careful not to make too much noise. I didn't want to wake up my parents or my brother. They would only torment me and ruin my mood.

Once I was dried, I programmed the CD player to listen to the Craig David song on repeat.

I methodically applied my makeup and got dressed in jeans, my black leather boots and my white Craig David t-shirt.

I went downstairs and poured myself a glass of pineapple juice. Every sip was a struggle due to my growing excitement. I couldn't even contemplate food. I wouldn't be able to drink the rest of the day as I couldn't risk losing my place in the front row if I needed the toilet.

I left the house at exactly 8. 45am. I tried to walk slowly and take my time but my feet had other ideas.

Denise was standing on the pavement outside her house. I guess she didn't want to wake her parents either.

'Hi, Denise, did you have a nice birthday?' She had turned sixteen the day before.

'It was okay. You'll never guess what Mum and Dad got me.'

'Um, series 5 of *Friends* on video?' I guessed that because I knew that she needed it for her collection.

'No, but I got that from my Gran.'

I was about to tell her, 'I give up,' when she pulled out a blue and silver device from the front pocket of her jeans.

'No way,' I gasped, 'Your mum and dad bought you a mobile phone?'

'Yep,' she answered as she flicked her long black hair. 'It's a Nokia 3210. And it comes with Snake.'

I was insanely jealous. I wasn't due to turn sixteen for another three months but I now knew what I would definitely ask for.

'Do you like it?' she asked as she stuffed it back into her pocket.

'It's alright,' I replied, feigning nonchalance. I was nauseated by her smug grin.

'So, who are you most excited to see at the park?' asked Denise.

'D'oh, ' I replied, pointing to my top.

'I thought it would have been Stephen Gately, ' she replied with a laugh. I could feel my cheeks blaze. I had gone off Boyzone in the last few months and I was embarrassed that I ever liked them. They were no longer cool to like.

'You used to like him too,' I replied. Denise remained quiet. She didn't like to be reminded of things like that. We stood in silence until the bus came.

We got off the bus opposite Graeme High School. We both groaned as we saw the place and tried to avoid looking directly at it.

'I can't believe that Monica and Chandler are engaged, ' I said as we made our way up the gravel path into Callendar Park.

'I know,' exclaimed Denise, 'but do you think they'll actually get married?'

'Yeah.'

'Why?'

'Because they have to,' I protested. I loved Monica and Chandler more than I loved Ross and Rachel.

'I hope *Friends* never ends,' I added.

'It won't, ' said Denise with conviction.

I looked at my watch as we entered the park. It was just after 9.20 am. The stage was set up to our right and there were shows to our left. The smell of hot rolls made my stomach grumble. The electronic sounds from the shows drowned out the quacking ducks at the pond.

The grass was mucky and we tried to avoid ruining our shoes. There were a few people walking about but the Park wasn't busy.

We walked over to Callendar House and sat down on the wall outside it. I always found it overwhelming that I had something so picturesque on my doorstep. This was where I wanted to get married.

The grass looked so fresh and healthy. The kids' park was abnormally quiet and there was no one on the golf course that we could see.

As there were no people hanging around the stage we decided to go and check out the shows, namely the Waltzers, Rib Tickler and the large Ferris wheel.

'So did you get anything else for your birthday?' I asked as we trudged through the mud.

'Nah, just boring stuff. But you know what I couldn't stop thinking?'

'What?'

'That in less than fifteen years I'll be thirty.'

I was puzzled why this would bother her so much. I mean, it was ages away.

'It really freaked me out,' she added. I nodded my head but I still didn't quite understand.

We spent the following half an hour wandering around the shows. I didn't want to go on anything as I was too anxious. We had a look around the stalls instead. My mum had given me ten pounds to make sure that I had something proper to eat. I bought some candyfloss.

I was intrigued by a dart stall. The main prize was a large blue elephant. Craig David was sure to notice me if I was holding a large blue elephant. I relayed my plan to Denise.

'Don't be silly. Do you think they'll let you stand in the crowd with an elephant? How embarrassing.'

'I won't be embarrassed and you'll want to come too when I'm invited backstage,' I answered. I could almost taste my confidence. Denise rolled her eyes at me and took two steps backwards when I handed over three pounds to the old man in charge of the stall. He handed me three darts in return. I had never played darts before in my life. I wasn't concerned though, I had fate on my side. If I won the elephant then I would win Craig David, I thought to myself.

'Okay, lady, hit 180 to win,' instructed the man.

I took aim and exhaled deeply a few times like I had seen them do on TV. I could barely hold the darts in my damp fingers.

I threw the first dart and missed the board. The next dart hit the number 1. Disappointment rose up my throat like acid. The third dart hit the bullseye.

'Congratulations,' said the man.

'What? Did I win the big elephant?'

'No,' he replied as he handed me over a smaller version about five inches long.

Denise grabbed my hand and pulled me in the direction of Callendar House.

'We better go if you want to be at the front,' she explained. I wanted to have another shot on the darts stall but she had a point. I stuffed the elephant into my duffel bag as we approached the main stage. We weren't the first ones there but we were right at the front.

'I can't believe I'm finally going to see Idlewild,' squealed Denise.

'Yeah I know,' I agreed. I had no idea who they were.

Within an hour there must have been ten thousand people behind me. We kept getting pushed up against the metal railings and I would end the day with severely bruised ribs and ringing ears.

'I canny believe there's nae security or that, ken what I mean,' said a guy behind us.

'If there's no security then I am going on that stage,' I whispered to Denise.

'There will be security,' she advised with another roll of her eyes. She had been to more gigs than me.

The security turned up about an hour later and had to pull the kids over the railings who couldn't handle life in the front row. I made a silent vow to myself that it wouldn't happen to me. I would endure the pain.

I was too excited for boredom to set in. About an hour before the concert was due to begin, I was struck with an idea. I took out the elephant from my bag, and a marker pen I had brought with me for all the famous signatures I planned to collect.

'What are you doing?' asked Denise. She had that worried look on her face, the one that said I was about to embarrass her.

'I'm going to write my name, address and telephone number on the label of this elephant. Then, when Craig comes on stage I'm going to throw it at him.' I was pleased with my great idea. I couldn't believe I hadn't thought of it before.

'Whatever,' chuckled Denise. I didn't care if I was embarrassing her. All I cared about was Craig.

It was difficult trying to write my details on a tiny piece of fabric with tens of thousands of people trying to usurp my position at the front of the stage. The only important part was that my phone number was legible.

I lost my pen in the madness of the crowd, however I had managed to jot down my details. I clung onto the elephant with all the strength I had left.

The concert began at exactly 1pm. I was mesmerised by how tall Jamie Theakston was in real life. He high fived Denise and I was so jealous.

The first couple of acts passed by in a blur. The crowd was jumping and the atmosphere was electric.

All of a sudden Craig David was in front of me. I started screaming as loud as I could and repeatedly jumped up and down. I was hyperventilating. I was so overcome with emotion that I couldn't stop a couple of tears from leaking out of my eyes.

I saw a girl on the big screen. She was sitting on a guy's shoulders and waving her hands in time to the music. She was wearing jeans and a red bikini top. It wasn't that warm.

'Let me up on your shoulders,' I shouted to Denise.

'What?' she shouted back with a shake of her head. I didn't know if she was referring to what I had said or if she genuinely hadn't heard me. I repeated myself.

'You can't get up on my shoulders, I can't manage your weight.' I was about to protest when the guy behind me picked me up. I screamed in equal shock and delight.

Craig sang a line and looked directly into my eyes.

This was my moment. I threw the elephant as hard as I could. It made it onto the stage and bounced off a small speaker. Craig seemed more interested in a black lacy bra that someone had thrown to him but I didn't mind, I knew he had a certain image to maintain.

My throw disrupted the man holding me and before I knew it I was on the ground. Luckily, my duffel bag broke my fall. I had lost my space at the front of the stage but I no longer cared. I had done what I'd had to do and Craig had noticed me.

A few minutes later, Craig finished his set and my heart nearly exploded in my chest when he picked up my elephant.

'He's got it, he's got it!' Denise and I screamed and clutched at each other.

'That's my elephant!' I screamed as loud as I could. Of course, Craig never heard me above all the euphoria.

With no regard to my feelings, Craig threw the elephant out into the middle of the crowd and promptly exited the stage with a final wave to his fans.

Even if I'd wanted to, I barely had a voice left to speak with on the way home.

As soon as I got in, I trudged upstairs to my bedroom and changed my clothes. My t-shirt ended up under the bed. I never wore it again.

I went downstairs to make myself some toast. My brother was listening to music in the living room.

'How was it then?' he asked.

'It was fine,' I lied, 'What's that you're listening to?' I asked, desperate to change the subject.

'Eminem,' he answered, 'A song called "Stan". That's what you call decent music.'

I had to admit, it sounded good.

Spring

Peter Callaghan

Bold brushstrokes
swirl in the breeze
bees busy-bob
from bud to bud

freshly cut grass
unearths diamond memories
of early morning baking bread
crackling coal, Friday night Musk.

Dad, a hulk in the heart
of a square lawn
casts a commanding shadow
over his regiment

of seeds, which soldier
through the hard earth
and charge towards the sun
shooting, forever shooting

dotted in dandelions and daisies.
Mum looks longingly from the kitchen
face aglow, like a little girl
twirling buttercups beneath her chin.

The wireless fans familiar tunes:
Stardust, Moonglow, Smile,
a basin full of foamy bubbles
clinks china cups. Then autumn

falls. Barren branches
scratch the clouds. Muddy puddles
scowl where daffodils danced
lone sparrows quiver

the line, unleash
a pearly curtain of tears
as they fly
in search of a crust.

My parents in armchairs slouch
transfixed by the flickering screen,
garden path footprint free
as summer sun jigsaws heartless.

Autumn snores into winter
short days, long nights
empty beds in empty rooms
where lullabies once hushed,

then spring squints an eager eye
between curtain cracks
clicks her ruby-slippered heels
and cartwheels gaily

through every doorway of the house
clatters letterbox, billows curtains
sweeps away cobwebs
of dust and doubt

Dad, a hulk in the heart
Mum looks longingly
then I come home
Mum hugs. Dad raises a hand.

"How are you doing?" I ask
"Oh fine," says Dad. "Fine.
I haven't died a winter yet."
The kettle whistles a brew.

In This Moment

Peter Callaghan

Hunkered down by the loch
rod in hand, he reels in the wilderness
like an artist: here
a thumb-smeared green

there, a scratch of thistle
above, bovril sky
below, a single orange bubble
afloat on charcoal grey.

No longer
the cocksure teddy boy
eyes furtive forward
fist triggered back.

Now he is
shuffle and sway
ribs unhinged, like an old
chest of drawers

ear-marked for the skip
forehead a noteless stave,
blue suede shoes shed.
Slip-ons instead.

Yet, hunkered down
a pebble among rocks, he is
perfectly poised; still
but for the tidal

drag
of a hand-rolled fag
pluming poetic smoke up
at a rulered 45.

In this moment,
what will be
hangs in the balance
unpainted by time.

In this moment,
my father
hangs forever framed
in my mind.

Enough Rope

Janet Paisley

'C'mere.' I wave Davie in. 'M'oan see whit I've got.' He cannae believe I'm up and awake. Wait till he sees why. I scuff oan aheid. Shovin ma feet intae tied shoes has long since broken the backs. Haen a massive belly doesnae make bendin easier – drug-induced obesity. Davie folleys, dodgin the hauf-fu bin bags lying aboot.

'Ye're supposed tae be ready for the golf,' he says. That's why he's here, tae pick me up. A favour, gettin me oot the hoose. We've been pals since school. Started Uni thegither, fifteen year ago, baith engineerin. I never got by second year. Ma brain caught fire, the hale world chynged.

In the kitchen, Davie clocks the foostie plates that litter the worktops. The room must stink. I bat awa the shame, too excited tae care.

'Ye'll no believe this.' I fling open the back door, and hurry oot.

Ahint me, Davie snorts. He thinks he's ready for onything, especially wi me. In oor student days, he tried tae make sense ae ma gibberish, or calm doon ma torment fae noises he couldnae hear. I squash them noo before they bother me. Doon the gerden, oan the gress, it stauns aboot three metres high, covered wi the auld hap I flung ower it efter I'd dismantled the packin and seen whit it was.

'Haud oan.' I motion him tae staun back, untie the auld towrope roon it, grab the plastic sheet and pull it aff. 'There ye go.' In the sunlicht, the silver dazzles.

Davie's chin draps. He stares, and stares. Ma face hurts fae grinnin.

'That's no real,' he says, shakin his heid. 'That cannae be real.'

'Real as you and me. It's yin ae thae maquettes, the wee yins. Braw, eh?'

'Wee? It must be ten feet tall. How the hell did it get here?'

I laugh oot lood. 'Fell aff the back ae a lorry.'

Davie's oan the phone right aff. 'Craig, ye need tae get up here.

No, we're no meetin at the clubhoose. No noo.'

Craig's ma brither, younger than us. I kin just hear him.' If he's aff his meds, I'm no dealin wi him. Phone his nurse.' That's ma community psychiatric nurse. But he's aw right, Craig. Helps me oot since oor Dad deid. Was livin here durin the worst years: the black moods; suicide attempts; the rage; brekin things; the suspicion. Aw the crazy stuff. Stop. I put ma face against the cauld, bright steel. Shut ma een.

'No, no,' Davie says intae the phone. 'He's fine. Happy as Larry. But ye need tae come. Ye need tae see this.'

Craig must be speakin noo. Davie looks roon the gerden, at the high fences, the trees. Naebody kin see us. Aw the same, he ducks his heid, lowers his voice. Actin like me noo, suspicious.

'It's a Kelpie. He's got a Kelpie.' Silence. 'So help me, Craig, I'm staunin lookin at it, in the back gerden. It's yin ae thae wee yins they made first.' Mair silence. 'Craig?' He shoves the phone in his pocket. 'Craig's oan his road,' he says, as if that solves somethin.

'Fine.' I stroke the horse's neck, feelin the panels, the spaces atween. It's the heid doon yin. Sunlicht glints aff it. 'Take a photie.'

'No. That's aw we're needin, proof.' But he pulls the phone back oot his pocket, takes twa or three. Bet they'll no be gaun oan Facebook, but. 'An stop touchin it,' he says. 'Ye're leavin fingerprints.'

'Magic, innit?' I wander roon it, lookin at the galvanised plates, the welds, its een, the twist oan its spiky mane. The spaces make the shape as much as the steel. It takes baith, presence and absence — silver and licht. Whit isnae there maitters as much as whit is.

It makes me special tae, no just a big, dirty fat man that cannae shower and shave or clean up his hoose. Says there's mair than hurtin, exhaustion, haen a heid fu wi stuff I'm ay fightin tae ignore or strugglin tae silence, feelin gaunt for aw ma girth, een starin doon a daurk tunnel that never ends.

The Kelpie chynges that, shaped wi air and metal, thoosands ae sherp edges turnt intae sweepin curves. It's fine, a fine thing.

Davie's back in the hoose, daen a Mrs Mop tae keep him awa fae the silver horse, fae touchin it, examinin it. I hear him scrapin plates in the kitchen, getherin rubbish intae binbags. He pops in and oot, crammin bags intae the green wheelie bin.

'I'll put this roon the front,' he says when it's fu, ''cause you'll forget.'

That's me pegged. He wheels it awa roon the hoose. I hear voices, real yins. Then he comes rushin back.

'There's a wife chappin yer door,' he says, grabbin the hap aff the grund and chuckin it back ower the Kelpie. 'She thought I was you.' He yanks at the edges, makin shair it's covered. 'Ye better go answer afore she comes roond.' He shoves me in the back door, shuts it ahint us.

Fightin doon the panic, I go tae the front door, open it. There's a wee wummin staunin there, wi moosy hair and glesses; comfy-lookin. She waves a caird.

'DWP,' she says. 'We wrote.' Yin ae thae folk that yaise initials, sense verboten. Thae letters dinnae mean whit ye think.

In the livinroom, Davie has opened the curtains. There's a pile ae letters, no opened, oan the coffee table. He must've sorted them oot fae the junk. They go back months. I dinnae want tae open them, but she needs me tae prove wha I am: bank statements, electricity bill.

'Who's that payment from?' She asks, sittin opposite, pointin at it.

'Ma brither,' I say, though I'd raither no tell her onything. 'It's for ma bedroom tax. Works oot aboot twenty pound a week. Craig peys it for me.'

'He lives here too?'

'Naw, got his ain place. Wife and weans tae. Since oor Dad deid, there's twa bedrooms spare here. I'm waitin oan a one-bed, but there isnae any.' I draw a deep braith. Think positive. 'I pey mair council tax noo tae. Get that masell.'

'I see,' she says, gien me back the statements. Nae comment aboot hoo the money comin in is less than the money gaun oot. Didnae used tae be. Is noo, nae maitter whit I dae withoot. Every time they name-chynge a benefit the money goes doon. Bills just go up. The less ye yaise, the mair it costs. They dinnae let their profits drap. I stare at the columns ae figures. Somethins no right. The wifie's checkin her ain papers. 'You get ESA and DLA.'

43

'No,' I shout. That was it. 'It's no here!'

'Pardon?'

'Ma Disability Livin Allowance. See.' I wave the aulder statement. 'It's oan here.' I wave the newest yin. 'But it's no oan here!'

'Are ye sure?' Davie asks, like he even kent whit I was talkin aboot.

'Sure, I'm sure.' I get up aff the sofa and pace aboot, tryin tae mind. A form came in. Big thick thing. Craig seen it, made me open it. 'I done the form. Craig helped. Taen us weeks.' I'm rakin aboot in ma heid, chasin memories that scuttle awa. It was ages ago. 'And we posted it, yin nicht when I was oot wi the motor.'

'Calm doon,' Davie says. 'Mibbe there's somethin in yer mail.'

The comfy-lookin wifie shoogles hersell, clears her throat. 'You'll be changing to PIP,' she says. 'They're experiencing delays.'

'And gein folk hert-failure,' I tell her. Ma hert batters.

Davie gets oot his chair. 'I'll get ye a coffee. Sit back doon.'

'If ye don't mind,' the wifie insists. 'This'll only take a couple of minutes.'

Davie waits till I'm sittin, then goes ben the kitchen. I draw some deep braiths, calm masell. She's watchin, writin it aw doon. Somethin tae laugh aboot efter, back at HQ. See, initials everywhaur. Ye huv tae watch. They creep in.

'And you get ESA?' She asks again, but it's no really a question. She looks rattled, no happy at bein caught oot ower the missin money, no while she's here onyroad. I ken whit's gaun oan noo.

'Aye. I'm in the support group.' There's a misnomer for ye.

Davie comes back wi coffee, sits it in front ae me, then plonks doon aside me tae look through mair envelopes fae the pile. White and broon. Some wi windaes. Some wi nane.

'And you work,' the wummin says, scribblin awa, 'for Swift Rescue?'

'No.' Is that the best they kin dae? 'That's Craig, ma brither.'

Davie backs me up, tells her I'm schizophrenic. 'No way he can work.'

She'll ken that. It's in ma records, diagnosis, symptoms, implications, how I cannae keep a routine, huv delusions, hallucinations, miss appointments wi doctors, dentists, ma nurse. I used tae miss the day hospital tae. We had groups for walkin, fitba, bowlin. But the cutbacks left them short-staffed. Noo there's haurly ony groups so I dinnae miss as many. Even golf. Yince a month Davie comes tae pick me up. Yin time in three I micht make it. Ye dinnae get in this shape by takin exercise. The no-sae-comfy wifie ignores Davie and carries oan.

'We've had a report that you do. You've been seen out in their breakdown vehicle.'

'Aye?' Yin for the psychiatrist, this. I huv tae swalley extra meds because I said they watched me. 'Craig comes for me if he gets a call-oot at nicht. He likes company. And I like gaun oot then. There's naebody aboot.' Folk are malicious, dangerous, ay whisperin ahint yer back, laughin at ye. No. Stop. Stop it. I stare at the wummin. Concentrate. Her glesses huv pink rims.

'You've a big heart.' She looks up fae writin, smiles. 'I wouldn't thank anybody for waking me up in the middle of the night.'

'Och, I'm no in bed onyway. No at nicht. Oan ma computer usually.' I dae withoot heatin tae huv the internet. It's ma social life.

'You must be a help to him though.'

'No much. I'm nae mechanic.' I need tae big masell up. 'Tie the straps. Pack up the tools.' I pat ma belly. 'Eat a few MacDonalds when the jobs are done.'

'I hope he pays.' Whit a wee terrier she is, gien me enough rope. The comfy look's a carefully calculated front. Her hair should be ironed.

'He does.' I grin back at her. 'He's the one wi the wage.'

'So you're not on the payroll?'

'No. Ye kin ask Swift if ye want.'

'We'll make enquiries,' she says, and hauds oot the note she's been writin. 'This is a record of what you've told me. If you would sign and date it.'

I dae that. Davie gies me a letter fae yin broon envelope then shows her oot. The letter's a receipt. They got ma form, three month ago. I kent I'd sent it. So they've stopped that money, half whit I get. This is no real.

Davie comes back in. He's relieved there was nae mention of Kelpies, had worrit the hale time the wifie would look roon the hoose and see it through the kitchen windae. He doesnae get it. She got whit she came for and couldnae escape quick enough. The hoose smells. Me tae. Ma hauns're shakin though. Useless, that's me. A useless eater. Breathe. Think aboot somethin else.

The front door opens, shuts. Craig comes intae the room, in his work claes, hair spikier than usual, lookin worrit.

'I brought the truck. We need tae get that ootae here.' He marches oan ben the kitchen, opens the back door, takes a look oot, swears, and cames back through. 'That's whit was in the box we picked up last night, a bloody Kelpie?'

'Ye picked it up?' Davie says. 'Whaur aboot?'

'The Falkirk Wheel,' Craig says. 'Bloke in the car park couldnae start his motor. I got it gaun and away he went. We're havin a smoke afore gettin back in the cab when a low loader drives oot the gates and away up the hill. Had two big boxes oan it. Once we get gaun, hauf roads up the brae, there's yin box sittin, naebody near, in the pitch daurk.'

'Telt ye.' I says tae Davie. 'Fell aff a lorry. It was a hazard. So we tied a rope roon it, and winched it aboard.'

'Had another call-oot come in so we dumped it aff here first,' says Craig.

'Stealin by findin,' Davie says.

'Naw, naw. Finders keepers.' I watch Craig. He's seen the mood I'm in, is checkin oot ma pill box. Mibbe I kin persuade him. 'It's just a wee yin.'

'Ye cannae keep a Kelpie!' Davie yelps. 'They'll be lookin for it.'

'These are yesterday's,' Craig says, handin me pills. 'And Davie's right. A box ae toilet rolls is one thing. But a Kelpie? Wee or no, it'll be worth a fortune.'

I ken that, of course. I'm ill, no stupit. There's nae keepin it. Come winter, when the leaves faw aff the trees, aw the neighbours'll see it sittin there in the gerden. Ye cannae always huv whit ye'd like. Besides, they come in pairs. Its wee pal wouldnae look right oan its ain, tossin its heid back, neighin at the sky.

'Better wait till night,' says Davie, 'drop it where ye found it.'

'And take the chance I'll no be seen daen it, or huvnae been?' Craig's no happy. 'It's a big truck.'

'Take it back tae the Wheel,' says I. 'Tell the truth.' I staun up, feelin awfy heavy. 'It was dangerous sittin in the road, and you hudnae time tae check whit it was till noo.'

'Aye,' Craig agrees. 'Tough it oot, and hope naebody calls the polis.'

Davie offers tae go wi him. Yince we get the Kelpie boxed and oan the motor, I'm left haudin the auld towrope we tied it oan wi first time, watchin them drive awa. I go back in the hoose, drap the rope in the hall, and go tae bed.

Screamin. The Kelpie rears up, whinnies. Hauns grab ma airms, haulin me under watter, draggin me deeper, chokin me. Shaddas loom ower ma heid. Yellin.

'Wake up! Wake up, ye're screamin.' It's Craig, shakin me.

'Whit? Why, why're you here?' I'm wringin wi sweat, the bed sodden. It's daurk. Ma hert's thumpin, stomach churnin. 'The Kelpie. Where is it, where'd it go?'

'Back where it belongs.' Craig puts the bedroom licht oan. 'I telt ye already. That was last week, mind?'

I dae mind. Doon at the Wheel they'd just found oot a Kelpie was missin when Craig turnt up wi it. The load had been in transport aw nicht, and the crew didnae check their cargo when they clocked aff tae sleep. Must've been efter breakfast they noticed they were a box short. Craig got a hero's welcome.

The room is still screamin. Ma neighbours noisin me up. I roll ower, haul masell roon, stare at the wall. They're aw in cahoots.

'Ae ye gaun shoppin?' Craig asks.

'Naw.'

'Get up then.' He goes awa doon stairs. By the time I get doon, he's made us coffee. 'Ye need sugar,' he says. 'And there's next tae nuthin in that fridge.'

'Look at me,' I rub ma belly. 'I'm a camel. Kin live oan this for months.'

'No ye cannae.' He shoves ma dirty claes along the kitchen table and sits doon wi his cup. 'And ye've no taen yer pills again.'

'I forget.' I forget whit day it is, if it's a different day. 'One time'll no make much difference.'

'Except it's no one time, is it?'

I drink ma coffee. He drinks his. We drink some mair.

'I spoke tae yer CPN,' he says.

Oh, here we go. Ma cauld sweat is instant. 'Whit aboot?'

'Yer benefits. The delay. No huvin enough money. The stress ye're under.'

'I'm awright. Guys at the groups've been left wi nane. Not a penny. Dinnae worry aboot me. I'm oantae them.'

'Ye're no oantae them.' He drinks mair coffee. 'The Council've got these Benefits Advisers. They kin chase things up for ye, sort things oot.'

'That would be guid.'

He relaxes, looks me in the eye. 'One ae them's gaunae come and see ye. Is that aw right?'

'Aye.'

It's no, but sayin it is keeps him happy. He's no oan call the nicht so he's gaun hame. He washes his cup. He must've washed baith tae make the coffee. His'll be the only clean yin in the hoose noo.

'Look, I'll take ye shoppin' he says. 'I kin gie ye the money.'

'Naw, ye're aw right. You've the bairns tae think aboot. I'm fine. We kin go next week, when I get ma,' I streetch the initials oot, 'EESSAA.' I grin, so he thinks I only did it cause it's a stupit name. Employment and Support Allowance. Why cry it that? It's for folk that arenae fit tae work. Should be cried Nae Employment and Precious Little Support Allowance.

'Dae somethin for me,' he says oan his road oot. 'Open yer letters when ye get them, at least the broon yins wi windaes. Okay?'

'Aye.' The door shuts ahint him. Ma ain brither, turnt against me, speakin their riddles, plottin tae get me back in the hospital, drive me mad. Fae ahint the wall, I hear chains rattlin, folk mutterin. I hit it a kick. In the livinroom, I pull the plug oot the phone. It's ay ringin. They kid oan they're tryin tae sell ye somethin, onythin, just tae wind ye up. Or I hear them oan the ither end, breathin, no sayin onything, just listenin. They'll need tae try some ither trick noo. I'm oantae them. Presence and absence. I'm no gaun back in the hospital, no for them. Nae wey.

The first broon envelope wi a windae that comes in is fae them. It says so oan the back. I prop it up oan the coffee table. Noo, if it says I'm gettin Personal Independence Payment, then I'm wrang, and Craig's still oan ma side. Even ma hauns are sweatin. I get some watter, take ma pills. The curtains are shut. They're never open. So's naebody kin see in. I pick the letter up. Put it doon. This is no easy. Come oan, come oan. Ye're a man no a mouse. Right, game oan. I grab it, open it, read.

Ma ESA's been stopped. *Failure to notify a change of circumstances… admitted you were in work… in receipt of regular monthly payments by direct debit… also payment in kind… possible cash in hand…*

Craig.

Och, Craig.

Ma hert hurts. A lump growes in ma throat. He could've just said, just telt me he didnae want me gaun oot in the motor wi him, that he couldnae pey ma bedroom tax onymair, didnae want some nutter bein uncle tae his bairns. Ma een nip. Big shudders shake ma chest. Ma belly heaves.

Yince I calm doon, I'm ready. They think they've got me noo. I'll sterve, or go nuts. Well, sod Craig. Sod the lot of them. The Kelpie was richt. I empty the fridge: yin ready-meal, a lump ae cheese, and I've twa slice ae breid left. Foodbanks are for folk that kin get there, run the street-and-strangers gauntlet. I cannae. Yin guy at oor group, he used tae eat toilet roll wi tomato sauce. Benefit spaghetti, he cried it. Stops the hunger, he said. I'm shair some ae thae ready-meal manufacturers are awready oan it.

When I'm done eatin, I take ma pills. It's like self-harm, takin these. That, and déjà vu. I lift the auld towrope fae the hall, go upstairs, get the stepladder fae the cupboard, and staun it under the loft hatch. The rope's rough and thick. I'm a big lad. But it'll be strong enough.

It's years since I yaised these steps. Huvnae been up the loft in a while. I shove the hatch open, throw the rope in, climb oantae the tap step and reach intae the opening, grabbin the edges for support. I heave masell up. Heave. Heave. Nut, it's no happenin. Ma feet are aff the step, but ma belly's stuck in the hatch.

Sweat washes ower me. Ma airms shake fae tryin tae haud ma wecht. I wiggle tae ease masell through. The widden hatch grips ma middle like a vice. Ma airms are easier but I daurnae let go. I kin haurly breathe. I hear a laugh. Laugh. Laugh. Laugh. They must be watchin up here tae. Stoor floats in the licht fae the skylight. Air. Licht. The beam I was gaunae tie the rope tae is richt above ma heid. The plan was tae drap doon through the hatch. Drap? I cannae move.

Heave. Wriggle. I'm stuck, cannae get ony further in. If I let go, ma wecht'll draw me doon. I'll faw, brek ma legs, ma back mibbe, clatterin doon wi the steps. Whit the hell kin I dae, stey here till I growe thin? Ma airms willnae haud me that long. Laugh. Laugh. Laugh.

'Stop it!' I roar. 'Stop, stop, stop!' I'm that stupit and useless I cannae even kill masell. The Kelpie was wrang, gein me hope when there's nane. There's nae absence, nae escape. A wheelchair'll make me even mair helpless. I draw whit braith I kin and roar and roar wi frustration. When I stop, they're mutterin at me fae the shaddas. 'Got ye noo. Got ye noo.' Somethin touches ma ankle, grips it. Fricht fires up through me. Baith ankles are gripped.

'It's okay.' Soonds like a wummin, muffled, shoutin. 'Can you lower yourself? I'll guide you to the step.'

I couldnae be less okay. Whit new hell is this? I let go and she's no there? She cannae be there, oan the steps below me. Nae real wummin would take the risk. Hauf a ton ae beef micht land oan her, flatten her.

'Come on,' the voice says. Ma ankles get a wee shake. 'It'll be okay.'

I'm no very good at trust. An illness like this teaches ye no tae. But voices cannae shake yer ankles. I wiggle a wee bit tae free ma belly back doon the wey. If she's no real, I'm gaunae faw.

'That's it.' The grip oan ma ankles tightens. I kin hear her better noo ma body's no blockin the hatch. 'Slowly does it. Keep coming.'

Ma airms are near gein up haudin me. Then ma taes touch the tap step. I'm oan it. The hauns guide ma fit doon tae the next step then let go.

'You're fine now. Okay?'

'Aye.' I hear her go doon aff the steps.

'Best shut the hatch,' she says. 'It's a fire hazard left open.'

Airms shakin, I slide it shut, and climb doon oantae the landin. The wummin's stood at the tap ae the stairs, skinny wee thing, pixie face, aboot the same age as me. I dinnae ken wha she is or why she's in ma hoose. I must look a mess, stoory, fat and stupit. She says her name. It means nuthin. She could be yin ae them.

'The Benefits Adviser,' she sticks her haund oot, 'from Falkirk Council? Your brother arranged for me to call.'

'So he did.' I shake her haund. Is Craig aw right then? 'You saved ma life.'

'Not at all. From injury, maybe. You're lucky. I knocked a couple of times. Was about to go away when I heard you shouting.' She heids doonstairs.

It wasnae laugh, laugh, laugh. It was knock, knock, knock. I hear it again. No fae doonstairs this time. Above me. In the loft. Horse's hooves clatterin oan the beams. Whaur the rope is. The Kelpie, waitin oan me.

'Gie it time,' it says. 'Ye'll get thin. Fit through the hatch.'

'I need help!' I yell, and scuff doon the stair efter the lassie. Let her be real. Please, let her be real. I need help.

Today's Special at the York Café

Helen MacKinven

In front of the Steeple, twa young lassies with smiles as plastic as a Barbie doll's stood in front of a folding table like the wan ah used for wallpapering. Their fake cheeriness wisnae enough tae tempt a couple of pensioners passing by with wee snippets of smoked salmon speared with cocktail sticks. The auld folk kept their heids doon and walked past muttering, 'Naw, thanks onywey hen.' Wan of the lassies had a bundle of leaflets but she wisnae having ony mair luck than her pal, who still had a plateful of fish. Baith of them wore aprons with a purple logo in the shape of a tree but instead of leaves the branches had a fish, a cut of meat, a strawberry and a stalk of wheat. As ah edged closer, ah could make oot a love heart in the tree design and the words, '*Year of Food and Drink, Scotland 2015.*'

First ah'd heard of it.

The lassie dishing oot the samples of salmon took a step forward.

'Would you like to try some of Scotland's finest smoked salmon?'

The slithers of slimy fish were honkin and gave me the dry boak. The stench wrapped itself roond me like a wooly scarf and ah felt masel gag.

'Naw, ye're awright. Ah'm no a lover of fish unless it's been deep fried.'

Her smile slipped but she wisnae givin up that easily.

'Oh go on, live dangerously! It's top quality home grown produce from Inverawe smokehouse.'

There wis nothing hame grown aboot her hoity toity accent. It sounded mair English than Scottish tae me, either that or she came fae Embra.

'Ah'll take a leaflet fae yer pal instead.'

Onything tae get her aff ma case. The other wan handed me a recipe card and ah kidded oan ah wis actually reading it, as if ah wis gonnae bolt straight doon tae Asda for the ingredients for smoked salmon parfait, pickled cucumber and spring onion salad, whatever the hell that wis. They should be teaching the younger wans tae cook a decent meal like mince and tatties instead of this nonense.

'Bon appetit!' she cawed efter me. Ah wisnae sure how tae pronounce *parfait* but ah ken that a French phrase wisnae gonnae sell Scottish food and drink. Aw this promotional guff ripped ma knitting; it would take mair than a campaign, posh recipe cairds and free samples tae boost trade in places like Fawkurt.

Ah walked past the empty Burger King, the windaes covered with Windolene the wey folk used tae white oot their windaes if they were decorating or had done a moonlight flit. Above the main doors there wis only a faint trace where the name and logo had once drawn in crowds, replaced noo with a 'To Let' sign. It shut doon ages ago. Even a massive American chain couldnae stay in business here. And it wisnae jist restaurants and bars that needed saved. The High Street wis deid, a ghost toon. The Works and Argos wis shutting their Howgate branch. Ower the last few months Michael Warren, Phones 4u and the Perfume Shop had all closed doon and even efter forty six years in business The Gilded Cage had shut. And noo that TKMaxx had moved tae the retail park there wis nothing worth stepping inside Callendar Square for, a white elephant since day wan. The only shops that were daein well up the toon were the charity and pound shoaps.

There wis a poster in Asda asking for donations for the Fawkurt food bank, saying that it gave oot three hunner food parcels a month. It's shameful that in this day and age folk across Scotland struggle tae feed themsels and their weans. Never mind smoked salmon, ordinary folk oan zero hours contracts and struggling oan benefits were grateful for a tin of Asda's Smart Price beans.

Families cannae afford tae eat in, never mind eat oot and even if you wanted tae go oot for a meal where would you find the best of Scottish food and drink? No in Fawkurt, that's for sure. A new place across fae the bus station had opened in the auld Callendar Arms called JD Rockets. Ah'd seen a photie advertising it in the Falkirk Herald. It wis an American 50s style diner like the wan in Happy Days with a jukebox and stuff oan the menu like Mississippi Cajun Chicken and Bourbon Street BBQ Roasted Vegetables. Whit wis that aw aboot? Certainly no celebrating Scotland's finest cuisine. Fawkurt hasnae jist loast its decent shops, it's loast its identity. The Fonz didnae live in Camelon. Real folk want real food.

Ah stoapped at the Bank of Scotland cash machine and withdrew a tenner. That wouldnae get me a main course and a drink fae JD Rockets. The only thing retro wis the décor. But everywhere wis the same: fancy menus and fancy prices. Where were aw the value for money restaurants cooking fresh food? Fawkurt had had some great cafes when ah wis younger. Behind the Steeple, the Tolbooth had done lovely homemade soup, ideal oan a cauld winter's day, or if High Tea wis mair yer thing then there wis the tearoom upstairs at Mathieson's the bakery for freshly-made tea, toast, cakes and scones. The waitresses in there wore proper uniforms, lassies smartly dressed in a black skirt, white blouse and frilly apron, nae polo shirts and baseball caps for them.

But the best place tae go for a Fish Tea wis the York Café, although some would argue that they preferred the cosy wooden booths in Moscardini's. Whichever chippy you rated the best, wan thing wis the same aboot them baith: you'd get a slab of battered cod, loads of hand-cut chips, proper chippy chips, fresh white bread and salty butter alang with a big pot of tea. Who could argue with that?

As ah slipped the tenner inside ma purse, ah wis aware that somebody wis waiting tae use the cash machine and when ah moved aside, ah instantly recognised a face that ah hadnae seen in nearly thirty years.

'Jeezo, how's it goin, Chrissy?'

It wis tempting tae gie her a big cuddle but ah'm no the air-kissing touchy feely type, ah'm fae Fawkurt.

'Ah cannae mind the last time ah saw ye but ye havnae changed a bit.'

In fact she seemed tae have improved with age: hair with blonde highlights, whippet-thin, designer handbag. You cannae hide money and she must have a loyalty caird for the sunbeds. Chrissy's phizog wis mair Oompa Lumpa than sun-kissed.

'It feels like a lifetime since anyone called me Chrissy,' she laughed as if ah'd said something funny. 'It's Christine. I'm really sorry, I recognise your face but I can't remember your name.'

How could she no remember me? Chrissy wis part of oor crowd, weekends up the toon shopping in Chelsea Girl then tae the Wimpy afore Coasters, and when we left school we graduated tae dancing and drinking at the Maniqui and Reids. We'd been oan hunners of nights oot the gether.

'Ah ken there wis plenty of nights oot we'd like tae forget but ye must remember hingin aboot with us – Jackie, Sharon, Michelle, Tracy and me, Linda.'

'Oh, yeah… Linda. You're looking… well.'

And whit did "well" translate as? Ah kent fine whit she meant: that ah'd a boady like a blancmange, bloodhound jowls and mair bags under ma eyes than Asda. There wis nae way Chrissy wis still eating burgers and fries. She snatched her money fae the machine and waved across at an eagle-beaked aulder wuman waiting ootside WHSmith.

'Linda, it's been brilliant to see you again and I'd love to catch up but I'm only visiting my mum for a few days.'

'Nae worries, it's been great tae bump intae ya. We should organise a wee reunion the next time ye're hame, eh?'

'Yeah, good idea. Well, gotta go, my mum's waiting for me. Bye.'

In heels so high you'd need breathing apparatus tae wear them Chrissy clip-clopped across the High Street leaving me wondering how a reunion wis possible if ah had nae contact details for her. But wan thing wis for sure, she'd left her FK postcode and pals fae the scheme behind.

Ah wandered up tae the York Cafe and stood ootside the mock Tudor building. Life disnae make promises but their menu did: *"Morning has broken but let our brunch fix it."* Brunch? The café wis still there but its spirit wis long gone.

The local landmark had been owned by the Serafini family for decades but wis taken ower a couple of years ago. Ah'd heard that the heart had been torn oot of the place. The café had been refitted with IKEA furniture, selling spicy fajitas and renamed a "bistro". Mair reasons no tae go back.

Ah hadnae stepped inside since ma Gran died. There were too many memories, maistly guid wans, but ah struggled tae forget whit an obnoxious besom ah'd been in ma teenage years: aw the moaning ah did and the hard time ah gave her oan oor last visit there.

The legendary York Café had been ma Gran's favourite café in the toon, and a chance tae spoil me. It'd been the same for every Fawkurt bairn who had grown up queuing for a cone and getting taken for a Fish Tea as a treat. In they days the chips at the York café had been chunky and mair like roast tatties than the French fries fae the Wimpy bar. The décor hadnae changed since ma Gran wis a wee lassie and some of the waitresses had looked like they'd served at the Last Supper. It wisnae trendy but that's the wey folk liked it, with its pink wicker furniture and mirrored walls. There had always been a queue tae get a table oan a Seturday.

Ah can still picture wan of the waitresses. She wis cawed Irene and had always patted her stiff hairdo as if she wis feart it might move. Ah'd seen her at the gala day oan the waltzer with her grandchildren and even when the guy had spun her car roond it didnae budge. She must've used a can-a-day of Elnett and ma Gran worried that she'd get too close tae the deep fat fryer and become a human fireball. She'd dyed her hair so black it looked blue and it wis shaped like a crash helmet. Aw that had been missing wis a strap under her chin. She'd served us the last time ma Gran had taken me there. The time we'd argued…

'Aye, ye cannae beat the York Café's chips, ' said ma Gran.

Ah shrugged. The queue for a table hadnae moved for hours. Well, that's whit it felt like. Oan oor left-hand side a wean wis swithering oer a ¼ of Soor Plooms or an ice-cream cone. Tae oor right the deep fat fryer sizzled as Irene picked up a tray fae the kitchen hatch, transporting the Fish Teas upstairs tae a table of hungry bairns.

'We would've got served quicker at the Wimpy,' ah sighed and added a dramatic Youth Theatre yawn.

'Wimpy? We're no gaun there. It's far too dear,' replied ma Gran.

'How would ye ken Gran? Ye've never even tried it.'

'Ah dinnae need tae try it tae ken that it'll be expensive tasteless rubbish.'

A mammy with twa wee wans joined the queue. Her message bag banged against me as she turned tae stoap the biggest wean fae nippin his wee brother. Then she skelped the back of his leg.

'But, can we no jist try the Wimpy for a change?' Ah eyeballed the greetin wean and gave ma Gran ma best begging face.

'Naw, ah like ye tae eat food that's guid for ye.'

'And how are the chips here any better than the Wimpy's?' ah asked.

'The York café's chips are very healthy.'

'York café chips, healthy? Ah've heard it aw noo.' Ah shook ma heid. 'Nae offence Gran but ah think ye're talkin mince.'

'Ye think ye ken everything these days. Well here's a wee surprise, yer auld Gran's no as stupid as ye think she is. The larger the surface area tae volume, the mair fat a chip will absorb. So these chips are much healthier than they French fries ye get at the Wimpy. Stick that in yer pipe and smoke it.'

She looked so chuffed with hersel and ah hated tae admit it but ma Gran's logic was right. Ah wis wan nil doon but ah wis determined no tae let ma Gran win.

Irene telt us a table wis free noo and ma Gran led the wey up the wrought-iron staircase. The tap flair wis mobbed and folk were aw chatting away while they got stuck intae their food. The only sound fae oor table wis the clink of cutlery oan plates.

'Yer face is tripping ye and it's putting me right aff ma Fish Tea, ' said ma Gran.

Ah stayed in the cream puff, refusing tae let her score anither point. But she wisnae giving in.

'And there's me thinking it wis a treat bringing ye here. Aw ye seem tae dae these days is moan. Ye used tae love gaun roond the shops with me and coming here every Seturday.'

Ah gave ma chips anither splash of vinegar and let her rant.

'Mibbae ye should go with yer pals tae the Wimpy instead fae noo oan. Ah can manage ma messages oan ma ain if ye dinnae want tae come with me ony mair.'

'Fine then! Ah've still got time tae meet ma pals, ' ah replied.

Ah stabbed a chip with ma fork but left it speared oan the plate.

'Ye're no gaunnae go the noo are ye?' asked ma Gran. 'Ye havnae finished yer chips.'

'Ah dinnae want these chips, healthy or no. Ah keep tellin ye that but ye dinnae listen. Ah'll get the bus hame masel.'

Ah sprang oot of ma chair, knocking ma glass of Irn-Bru ower. The orange liquid spread across the glass-topped table and ma Gran rushed tae mop it up with a paper hankie. Ah left her dabbing a stain oan her sleeve, wan that never came oot efter washing.

She never mentioned that day again, never asked me tae go shopping again and never took me back tae the York Café.

Aw ma Gran had wanted wis tae be with her precious granddaughter.

Aw ah wanted wis tae be with pals who wouldnae forget ma name.

Beyond the York Café there wis a McDonald's and a Greggs. Fast food chains, the kind of places ah wanted tae see in ma toon as a teenager, no quirky cafes with ancient staff. Now Ah could've been in ony toon in Scotland. The Wimpy wis gone and so wis ma Gran. Ah wished ah could sit opposite her again in the York café and treat her tae a Fish Tea.

Ah joined the queue in Greggs and ordered a Steak Bake. It burnt the roof of ma mooth.

Bruce's Taxis

Samuel Best

I sit back in my seat, adjusting the seatbelt as it cuts across my chest. The nylon's caught my throat and I reckon it'll leave a mark. Across from me, Niall's draining the last of a near-flammable mix of vodka and coke with heavy gulps. He's started early, and strong, and there's a part of me wary of where this night could lead us. Or him, rather.

'You'll need tae finish that, pal,' the driver says, and Niall waves his hand, still drinking, his Adam's apple moving quicker.

'City Nightclub, ta,' I say, and as Niall holds the empty bottle up like a child showing off to a parent the driver guns the engine and we're off.

'Out for anything special the night, boys?' the driver asks, scenes of Linlithgow High Street blurring past us, the reflection of streetlights and restaurant signs fuzzy through the rain-mottled glass.

'Jist payday, ken?' Niall says. He rubs his hands together, greedy-like, and the driver nods.

'Ken whit's weird?' Niall starts. 'See how it's called City Nightclub, aye? How come Fawkirk's no a city?'

'Is it not?' I say. 'Seems like a city, doesn't it? A small one, but still a city.'

'Exactly. I mean, as far as I ken, it's no a city. Jist weird the club's called City. Like, who thought ae that? It'd be like gontae Glasgow an gontae a club cawed, like, Toon.'

'Who decides what's a city and what's a town?' I ask.

'Dunno. Clearly someone no payin attention, like. An how comes places like Glasgow and Edinburgh get made cities but places like Fawkirk dinnae? I mean, how d'they decide?'

'Is it not something about needing a church or something?'

'Eh, Ben, look nae further. It's cawed Faw-kirk fur a reason. Place is teemin wae churches. An it's no like it's lackin in, ken, *historical clout*, is it? Battle ae Fawkirk. Battle ae Fawkirk Muir. Who's buried in the graveyards? Great Scottish heroes whit fought fur this country. No even jist that, but descendants ae King James VI. I'd say that's a pretty gid reason tae be taken seriously, would ye no?'

'Aye, yeah, I see your point. I mean, Linlithgow's a Royal Burgh. Stirling's a city. Why is Falkirk just a town?'

'When it's no *jist a town*, is it? Even mair recent than aw ae that, Fawkirk was where aw ae the iron wis gettin made, where oor canals were started. Ken streetlamps got invented here? It's a total hub. It's a centre ae things. It's no cawed *Central* Scotland fur nuthin, right?'

We're on the back roads now, rolling hillscapes lost to the darkness. The glow of Whitecross in the distance. To our right, the hum of the motorway. Through the trees I can see taillights flicker by as they outstrip us, and I can feel my pulse grow faster. We're close now. Predators lurking in the long grass near our prey. City Nightclub like a gazelle, grazing quietly until we arrive.

There's a lull in conversation and the three of us all have our eyes fixed on the road. Despite the music on the radio, the lull grows to this hulking mass and I try to fight it but can't quite hold back the words and I cringe as I hear myself ask the driver if he's been busy tonight.

'Aye,' he says. 'Seturday's ayeways busy.'

The lull returns, magnified, and I remember why you're not supposed to ask that in taxis. It always makes things worse.

'Gid chat here, eh?' Niall mutters and I glance over at him. He's staring at the back of the driver's head with a focus so strong I wouldn't be surprised to see smoke. He looks over at me quickly, then darts his eyes back to the lights outside. Something in my stomach tells me that this is the start of it, that tonight is already veering off course. The driver keeps his gaze on the road, oblivious, but I've seen it enough times to spot the signs.

We merge onto the motorway and the driver puts his foot down. We're speeding along, the hum of the tires on the tarmac like a soundtrack, merging with the thumping dance songs on the radio. Beside us Westquarter, Redding, Laurieston. Wee places. Places with people who live lives and who smile at their happy memories and cry at their sad ones. People who raise a glass to cheer their victories in life and who work to etch out a small part of the world they can sleep in safely. It doesn't have to be Falkirk. None of this has to be Falkirk. But it is. Tonight it is Falkirk. And I can't help but wonder why Falkirk isn't a city for all of this.

We spin right at the roundabout and now we're really here. The darkness stopped way back at Whitecross because Falkirk is neon. Falkirk is electric. Falkirk is buzzing with people out to have a good time. Falkirk could be the centre of the world tonight, and tomorrow... Tomorrow brings a new sun. A dawn full of stories. Good, old fashioned folk tales with drama and characters and punchlines, and people will gather together to tell these stories for years to come. Mind that time when? Where you there when? There was this one time when.

'Here, driver, how come it's called Bruce's Taxis?' Niall says, leaning forward between the front seats. My stomach clenches at where Niall might steer this conversation and I'm already trying to work out ways to save it. 'Is that, like, the local connection? Ken, bein so close tae Stirling? A bit ae Central pride?'

'Whit?' the driver says, his eyes flicking to Niall in the mirror.

'Ken, Robert the Bruce, King ae Scotland, defender ae independence. I wis jist wonderin if it wis a kindae nod tae that. Bruce's Taxis, like, defendin your independence by drivin you aboot Central Scotland. Fawkirk tae Stirling quicker than a horse.'

The driver shakes his head. 'I think it's cause the boss is called Bruce, pal, but I dunno. I'm jist here tae drive, eh?'

I laugh, a flutter of relief in my chest as Niall sits back in his seat, happy to let the questions fizzle out, his head nodding, considering. The taxi slows and pulls into the stream of traffic. Not regular traffic though, just other taxis for miles, all creeping forward, their meters ticking up with every millisecond, queuing to get as close to the club as possible so no one gets caught in the rain.

'Here we go,' Niall says, his seatbelt already unbuckled. We're still a long way off yet but he's itching to get in there. I think about what he said about the Battle of Falkirk and its arguably better-received sequel, the Battle of Falkirk Muir, about all of these regular people who came together under the banner of men they were prepared to lay down their lives for, about the reputation the Scots had in battle:

fearsome, fearless, itching to get in about their enemies, never mind sending them home to think again. Maybe it was right here that those battles were planned, or fought even. Maybe it was these streets that ran with the blood of men defending their home towns. These very pavements etched atop the graves of Falkirk's fathers and sons, mothers and daughters.

'See, look about ye,' Niall says. 'Look at aw these people. These beatin hearts. How can anyone look at places like Fawkirk an no see the same things they see in Glasgow, in London. Or further afield, in New York and Berlin. In Cairo and Stockholm. Aw Fawkirk needs is an underground service an a bunch ae dodgy bankers an it'd be a city jist like the rest ae them.'

The driver chuckles to himself and I can see his grin in the rear-view mirror.

'I'm no jokin,' Niall continues. 'Whit difference is there, really, between someone fae Camelon and someone fae Camden? Folk are aw born the same. We aw die the same. It's jist how you spend the middle bit that varies. Solidarity, man. Solidarity. Global unification. Be the master ae your own fate. Shopworkers ae the world, unite! Govern yourselves. Dinnae be afraid, is whit I'm—'

'Sorry, pal,' the driver cuts in, 'It's just you with aw this soft *we're all something special* nonsense. I dinnae mean tae burst your bubble here, ken, but d'you really think that's true? Do you think that's whit the boys in London, in Westminster, think? Bet you they don't think they're the same as you. Bet you they see you an all ae these people goin on your wee nights out, havin a few drinks tae loosen up, an rub their hands thegither, thinking "Aye, that's right, you have a drink. You have a drink and dinnae worry yourself aboot whit we're up tae. We're runnin the country here – you wee folk wouldnae understand." Regular people aw might be the same, but the folk at the top arenae the same as us.'

'That's no really whit I was gettin at, driver. We aw ken there's bother doon in London. I'm talkin aboot social politics right here, right now, no aw that Hoose ae Lords shite.'

'No no, it aw bleeds intae itself. There's you talking about aw the culture and community you find in places like this, but look whit happens every Seturday night. 7pm comes and you're all oot here gettin full. Prove them wrang, boys. Away an dae somethin different with yoursels, eh? Wake up. Take the power back.'

The traffic ahead stops to let another load of people out at City and in a heartbeat Niall's pulled his door open and he's away. I scramble after him, almost taking my own head off on the seatbelt as I go, and behind us I can hear the driver yelling threats. How he'll get us one day. His pals have done time for battering folk like us. We bolt round the corner and City looms into view. A snake of people winds its way from the doors out along the street and breathless, we head into it.

*

The music is so loud we're speaking right into each other's ears in the hope enough of what we say will come across to make sense. The worst situation for an argument, amplified by the number of drinks Niall had drained before we'd even left. 'You could have at least given us some fucking warning, Niall,' I shout.

'Aye, an how wis I gonnae dae that? Lean over an say "Here, Ben, we're no payin for this cab cause the driver's been a prick since before I even buckled my seat" ?'

'What are you on about? He just told you to finish your drink, man. Were you ever going to pay him?'

'Everyone drinks in taxis, Ben. Fucks sake, the guy was jist bein a total fascist. He deserved it. And anyway, it's no exactly like it's big money, eh? I'm hardly dodgin millions here.'

'Look, we've both been drinking, let's just leave it, yeah? I'm not going to get into the ins and outs of taxis and fascism with you now.'

Niall's chewing the inside of his mouth the way he does when he's considering something hard. Nods his head slowly. Eventually he shrugs and looks to the bar. 'You coming, then? Or are we no allowed tae drink in here either?'

'Don't be a prick. What are you having?'

'Double vodka and coke, ' he says, and he follows as I push through the crowd. The buzz in here is like an ocean. Vast. Overwhelming in the sheer magnitude of it. Floating in the tide around us are hundreds of bodies. A sea of folk out to etch memories from the night. We reach the bar and order drinks, and I watch as Niall turns to take the club in. His eyes sweep from wall to wall and it's like he's a king surveying his territory, a dangerous king, a king pulsing with energy and anger but with no way of expressing it properly. A part of me wonders what makes Niall tick, and another doesn't want to know.

He takes his drink and swallows a third immediately before stepping out onto the dancefloor, his glass raised high so it doesn't spill. We reach a little clearing and Niall stands, arms wide, and spins in a slow circle, nodding his approval. After two turns, he stops and clamps one hand round the back of my head. The song changes and a cheer goes up from the crowd.

'This is it, man!' he shouts. 'This is living!'

And in that instant, I'm there with him. I feel alive and young and energetic and brilliant. He grins and I grin back and I remember that we're best pals. Friends til the end. We both take a drink, the fizz fuelling the fire in our bellies, and I think that as much as he's my friend, it's just a shame he's such a dick.

Day Trip

Bethany Ruth Anderson

'Cheers, hen.' The man shuffled onto the seat at our table, but Jess, typically, grimaced at the word. She always hated when people called her hen – what am I? A chicken? Do I lay eggs? She rested her red Michael Kors handbag on her lap.

'We've only got a couple more stops.' I smiled and nodded in a way that I hoped seemed reassuring, though really I was rather enjoying the way she squirmed in her seat. Her eyes flickered across to the man beside her every now and then, taking in the tatty polo shirt, the dirty now-grey Adidas trainers, and the blue and white scarf hung loosely around his generous chin. There are thousands of men in Scotland that look exactly the same as that guy, but still she looked at him like an alien anomaly had somehow made it onto the train.

Jess huddled closer to the window, pointedly ignoring the man beside her. 'You missed a pretty good party the other night. I mean, some of them, you know, the ones from the Philosophy course? They were utterly boring. To be fair, they were on Danny's weed. That stuff makes everyone boring.' As if to emphasise her point, Jess fanned her manicured hand over her mouth in an empty yawn.

'Danny was there?' My eyes were firmly fixed on the passing scenery, aware that my enthusiasm would show in patches of pink on my cheeks.

'He's always everywhere. If you know what I mean. Seriously. Amanda Livingston was crying half the night, drinking AfterShock. That is literally disgusting.'

The noise I made was, I hoped, completely non-committal. Instead of thoughts of Danny, I replaced my focus with the streaks of rushing scenery. Far from a painter's inspiration, the train pulled us past stretches of empty green and brown fields, clusters of buildings dumped along the railway tracks, gloomy clouds that threatened rain: humdrum landscape of the Central Belt.

The next stop is Falkirk High. She looked at me hopefully, and when

I nodded that yes, this was our stop, she quickly gathered up her belongings and sat up straight, eager to alight. Once we were onto the platform, stuck behind the waddling polo-shirt guy, Jess looked left and right. Then her shoulders finally deflated. 'Oh, we're here.'

'Yup, the first point of our tour – the train station.' A bridge, a box with some chairs inside, and a platform going to Glasgow, the other one to Edinburgh. 'We'll get a bus and I can show you around on the grand tour.'

Jess had been on board with the idea. She'd thought it nice that I'd invited her away for the day, had said that she really ought to see how people in Scotland lived. After she used the word "privileged" I more or less stopped paying attention. But she'd agreed to go to the place where I'd grown up, and was looking forward to seeing another part of the country. "Another", because she'd never been anywhere other than Edinburgh, like most of my fellow students.

The weekday afternoon bus contained a couple of elderly women discussing their loot from their recent Asda shop, and a mother with a gurgling toddler on her lap. We took a seat towards the back of the bus, and I ushered Jess in next to the window so that she could get a better look at the foreign landscape. As the bus pulled further up the brae, Jess sat straighter in her seat, an expression of quiet surprise on her face, 'I didn't think this place would be so much like the countryside. It's actually quite nice.' That, I supposed, was as far as the compliments were going to go on this journey. But in Jess's books, "quite nice" was better than many things.

'My back garden faces a field,' I said. 'There are always sheep getting their wool stuck in the fence.' *As well as Irn Bru bottles, faded crisp packets, crusty receipts....*

Jess smiled, quite comforted by this thought, and enjoyed the rest of the bus journey in silence. Towards the top of the brae I motioned that it was time to get off and when we did she was less sure of her surroundings.

We stood at the edge of a wide, busy road, one that I hadn't been allowed to cross on my own as a child. On the side opposite stood uniform terracotta houses, a reasonably pretty slice of surburbia, the large front gardens well looked after, flush with green and promising hints of flowering colour. Jess looked up and down the road, searching for a place to cross the divide between one side of the village and the other.

'It's this way,' I said, turning and walking into the expanse of grey in front of me. Reluctant, Jess took a breath before following on beside me.

Growing up here, the layout of the village didn't make sense. It seemed deliberately cruel. On one side, separated from me by that busy main road, were streets lined with the kinds of houses that children draw when they think of houses. These houses, on the edge of the pebbledash scheme, were never the kind drawn in crayon. Pale, dirty brown and grey boxes, neatly lined up. No bay windows here, or pretty little porches, just flat stucco walls. There were gardens in the front, some which were lined with optimistic daffodils, the occasional gnome or ceramic hedgehog. Some instead were strewn with broken prams, battered kites, garden chairs that lay on their sides, covered in grime.

Here, on a weekday afternoon, some living room curtains are open to reveal scenes of soaps on television screens, women ensconced on sofas. Other curtains are still drawn, some of which I know are never open. 'What people do in their own houses in their own business,' Dad would tell me when I was younger. As I grew up, I learned to know what that meant, what possible secrets people might hide; a spectrum of abuses and addictions.

'This is like that programme we watched...' Jess walked close beside me, glancing at faded Neighbourhood Watch signs. If you did anything out on the streets here, you can guarantee that someone was watching.

'What programme?' Though I could guess the type she meant; there are enough of them these days.

'That one with the single mother with the four children and she couldn't get a job because she had to stay at home to look after all of them and the father of two of the children was in jail and the other one had disappeared.'

It was just like that. That, and so many other stories, sometimes kept quiet, sometimes brought to the light by gossiping and screaming in the streets, or the arrival of police. 'People don't really choose to live here, you know. It's where people end up.' In front of us was my childhood home, the same dappled grey as the houses on either side of it. There was the familiar dip in the plastic fence where bairns sat like craws waiting for the icecream van, fists full of grubby change.

As if on cue, a group of primary school children came running full pelt down the hill, arms spread out with their coats like capes, swooping with sounds of zooms to help them run faster. They disappeared into houses, yelling greetings to their mothers before the doors had even closed behind them. A small, frizzy-haired girl stared at Jess and I before rushing up the steps and into the door in front of us.

'We used to live there.'

'Oh.'

The revealing of my old home was an awkward situation for Jess, who was no doubt trying to think of something nice to say about the peeling red paint of the door. 'But not anymore? So we can't go in?'

'No. It's a three-bedroomed house. Council take it back if any of the rooms aren't being used. My parents couldn't just decide they wanted a study and a games room.'

'Really? That's a bit harsh.' I wasn't sure if she meant the council being able to do what they wanted with it, or that my parents were denied any extra luxury rooms.

The little girl's face appeared at the living room window, cheeks pressed up against the glass, her breath clouding it white. With a finger jabbing towards us, I turned to nod up the hill. 'Let's go to the park.'

Jess seemed brightened at the prospect, and walked with a slightly quicker step, slowing only to stare at hyper children tumbling in gardens, or kicking footballs against the kerb. The park, in its clearing of bushes, was of course full by the time we reached it: a mother helping a small boy down the rusty slide, a group of olders boys fighting with sword-sticks near the bushes, girls collecting little red berries in their t-shirts, the swing set being used as a climbing frame, each swing wrapped in its chains along the top.

'This is your park?'

'We used to come here all the time, and make little dens over there,' I pointed to a gap in the bushes where the girls were running with their loads of berries and leaves. 'We used to get properly clarty, but it was worth it.'

Jess stared at me that way she did whenever I used a word that wasn't within her lexicon, but I couldn't be bothered explaining it to her. I'd come here for myself, I realised. Not for her sake. She stood anxiously hugging her handbag to her side, then slipped her phone from her pocket, checking messages, checking the time.

I remembered the first time we'd taken the train through to Glasgow together. As we passed the grey flats of Hallglen, I'd pointed them out, saying, 'That's Falkirk.'

'That's where you're from?' At such a realisation, Jess's face had crumpled into a picture of misery, the same face that she used when watching charity ads, or those clips in between the funny stuff on Red Nose Day. Her hand had reached out across the table, touching my arm. 'That's amazing.' She spoke as though I ought to bask in her compliments, to know that I really deserved the praise, 'That's amazing that you got to where you are today, coming from that.'

"That" being a world unlike her own: no private education, no apres-ski in the Alps, no surprise trust funds. But there I was, just the same. Despite it all, she and I were granted entry to the same university – just as good as one another, regardless. How much did the money matter, Miss Jess?

So I'd shown her. And she was bored now, thumbing through her Facebook feed, no doubt disappointed that there had been no selfie opportunities on this trip.

'Such a sad place,' Jess offered, as we headed back towards the bus stop. 'Just so full of sad people, you know?'

But I was thinking of making castles out of milk palettes in the bushes, of playing kerbie in the street, of running home from school at the end of the day, of sneaking into the fields to follow the sheep.

Homecomings

Constance Saim-Hunter

On foot

The fog was tingly, slightly puzzling and surrounded me with damp penetration. The limp air made breathing harsh. Most of the others had already set off but I lingered, holding onto the black railings at the big gates to Victoria School. My Fair Isle bonnet, knitted last winter and now a bit wee, clamped my ears and muffled even more the soft sounds around me as I set off along Thornhill Road. Victoria Park had disappeared, just the low wall guided me along the pavement to the Belisha Beacon at Ladysmill and the safety of the Lollipop Man.

Ye're awfy late hen. Yer Mam'll be wonderin whaur ye've got tae. Awa ye go hame noo.

Woodburn Road and Montgomery Street, each house with a hedge wheremy mittened hands trailed to keep me straight. Despite the, once again hand-knitted Fair Isle mittens, my hands were drippy cold. Not like in the mornings when I'd clutch two copper pennies hot from the top of the cooker to pay the three ha'penny fare on the bus ride to school. Most houses had lights on but the eerie mist was hardly broken around the street lamps. In time with my footsteps I whispered some of my favourite words, letting them roll around my mouth – 'gob-bly-dook' was the best but 'per-ni-cke-ty' and 'com-pen-dium' were exciting too. Past the Nursery, I started to run on this more familiar part of the road. . Running blind but determined to get home as my hands groped for the hedges, crossing Alexander Avenue to the pavement still showing the chalked beds from yesterday's game, and up the path. Home.

– Is that you, hen ? C'moan get yer duffel coat up on the pulley. It's yer favorite the night, SMT.

Aye, Soup, mince and tatties. I was home.

By bus

As the bus pulled into St Andrews Square I opened bleary eyes, dragged the sleeves of my ratty musquash coat back up and lit a Camel. The foggy fug of cigarette smoke had surrounded me for the past twelve hours since leaving London the night before. I was almost there, and the Edinburgh voices around me sounded familiar. Just the Falkirk bus to find. The journey had started twenty-four hours earlier from Paris on the Gitane-and-Gauloise smoky coach to Calais, then the open deck of the ferry from there to Dover. Most of the time I spent on the deck being alternately sick over the side before slumping back down to light yet another Camel. Aye, going home was fun back in the Seventies.

Falkirk bus station on a Sunday morning hadn't changed much. Too early for behatted church-goers, too late for stoatin laddies running for the last bus to Slamannan or the disappointed lassies leaving Doakses without a click. Excitement made me fumble for the one and only pound note I knew had been somewhere at the back of my wallet for the past year and a half, although the bus conductress wasn't too happy about me taking all her loose change. This bus too smelt of sick and cigarettes. I was bursting with all the things I wanted to tell them at home about my life in Paris: the cafés open to the street, the jazz clubs in the Latin Quarter; my studio flat (really just a room but "studio" sounds better) up five flights of wobbly wooden stairs; the Turkish toilet on the landing shared with some very spooky characters from the other five rooms on my floor, the paté, le camembert, courgettes, sea-food. I'd tell of these things words tumbling out, mixing French with English, but not of my live-in lover nor the mugging I'd suffered my first week there. Some things had to be glossed over.

Getting off the bus at the fire station I crossed over to our street looking down to the tunnel under the railway line. In later years some educated moron would paint on the Laurieston side: 'Abandon hope all ye who enter here.' My Mam, trying to be posh, always told us to tell people we lived 'opposite the ice-rink' which I dutifully did all through High School. They would invariably answer 'Aw aye, the Bog

Road, ' or worse, 'the Boag'. Still looking up to the tunnel, I hitched my rucksack over my shoulders, wondering why on earth did I'd had to buy so many heavy presents. Through this tunnel lay a wonderland of fields, the Piggery, the burn and the spring where we drank the icy water in cupped hands, swearing it tasted better than Irn Bru. From the coo-park was a vision of Mordor: the tanks, chimneys and entangled pipes of the BP in Grangemouth belching flames and steam.

Behind the council-green front door I knew the whole family would be there in the kitchen ready to hear my stories, laughing at me struggle to find the right words after a year and a half speaking only French. As I opened the door, my Mam was in the lobby to greet me. No hugs, no gallic kissing of cheeks but a huge smile on her face.

– Is it you hen? Hoo wiz the trip? Still wearin that auld fur coat. Thought ye'd be a real Parizi-hen by noo!

My Dad and my five brothers and sisters were all there in the kitchen. The kettle was on and the smell of burnt toast lingered in the warmth of this noisy, crazy heart of our house. Tears didn't quite drop. I was too busy hugging, blethering and laughing. Aye, I wiz hame.

By car

Three weans strapped in the back up to high doh after the never-ending drive up from Portsmouth. As the first road-sign indicating FALKIRK appeared on the motorway I was high-dohing it too. Almost there. It had been four years since our last trip although during this time most of the family had turned up in the summers like swallows flying back every year to feast and burn in the hot Vendée sun. Without really realising it, I'd missed Falkirk and home. Bringing up the kids, answering every question, I'd grown up a bit too. Why is this right, wrong, stupid, good, bad, unfair, funny, frightening, beautiful, forbidden…? I'd had to make things clear in my own head before filling theirs with haphazard answers. Some questions are easily answered, others take time and thought. Why exactly did I vote for François Mitterand, why don't we live nearer Grandma, why are clouds pink in Scotland? How long is a piece of string? At times I'd say « well just BECAUSE » but often putting an answer in words defines an up till then gut-feeling.

The chattering in the back seat was turning into a full-blown argument as the girls pestered their wee brother with tales of wee boys in skirts. There's no French word for kilt so the conversation was interspersed with « le kilt », « Falkeerk » and « Grammmma ». Although the girls spoke some English (with a definite Falkirk accent) their wee brother at four had systematically favoured French. Turning, thank God, into Alexander Avenue with not a kilted man in sight, I was telling him it was just for one day at the wedding in the Highlands that we were going to next week that he would wear a kilt. This fourth or fifth hand-me-down from his cousins was in Grandma's house and we wouldn't be taking it back to France for him to wear. For the French, all Scots wore « le kilt » drank « le whisky » and lived in « un chateau » in a sub-region of England. My kids knew better. They'd heard me explain a million times that no, I was not English, that I only drank wine, that Great Britain and England are not the same thing...

As we drew up to the house, my Mam was sitting on the doorstep. She called something in the door as we unstrapped the boiling hot kids who pushed and thundered up the front path to jump on their Grandma. I lingered, getting cases from the boot and gulping down the hot rush of tears, then grinning as my brother appeared at the door with a tray of five glasses of Irn Bru each brimming over with a dollop of ice-cream. Brilliant.

Over the next three weeks we traipsed about Falkirk when not eee-yoochin at weddings, aw-dearying at a funeral and partying with the American, Australian, and otherwise worldwide cousins, brothers and sisters. Everyone seems to love Falkirk and leave it. As we wandered around Falkirk the kids listened to me, regretting some of the changes. No more Irn-Bru factory in Coburn Street, no familiar faces above the maroon High School blazers that I couldn't help scrutinizing, feeling sure I would recognise *somebody*. The absent chimney stack at the Brewery left a gaping hole in the sky not quite filled by the vile supermarket in its place. No more strong smell of god-knows-is-it-yeast as you wait at the bus stop. In fact, no more bus stops where you think they should be, shouldered out by new roads and roundabouts.

There's no word for home in French, just the more impersonal « chez moi ». For years I had a split-personality relationship to the words I used when speaking of my original home in Scotland or of the place I lived, worked, and loved in France. Home was both places. They were both mine, but for a time as I taught the kids to lift their eyes to the cupolas and turrets of my hame-toon and see their beauty on every street corner in Falkirk, my schizophrenic « chez moi » was here and now. We were home.

By plane

The pilot must have heard my prayers. On the approach to Edinburgh Airport he took the plane up the Forth, swooping over the bridges before banking left and down to Turnhouse. This was my favourite way home. It was cold, it was wet, and I could hardly see the bridges anyway for the tears streaming down my cheeks. The young lad next to me poked his girlfriend's arm as they exchanged a WTF look. They had probably just been away for the weekend to Paris and were coming home. But I was *really* coming home.

But what is home? Is home the place where you lived when you were young? Is home the place where you were born? Is it the place where your ancestors lived, worked, fought, loved and died? Is it the place where you go to sleep at night? Is this where your loved ones are? Is it the place you return to seeking rebirth? Or is it just the place you return to?

I was still searching for answers as I grabbed my case and pushed past the glaikit couple to be one of the first off the plane. No bags to pick up. Once again, it was just me and my wee suitcase, though I was no longer wearing a politically incorrect fur coat. I headed for the drop-off/pick-up and the welcoming arms of my six-foot and something wee brother. It was cold, Scottishly cold, and I almost regretted that old coat. The sun glittered on the snow at the top of the Ochils as we drew nearer to Falkirk. I love those hills. They're always there sheltering, menacing, glowing, like sleeping giants protecting Falkirk. They could be grey, purple, white, shrouded in mist or invisible in the rain but always drawing your eyes to them. On the road to Kincardine, from the top of Vicar Street, from up the braes, from our house, they had always surprised me and given me a warm snuggly feeling. The Alps are sharp and frightening, the Pyrenees are cold and brooding but the Ochils are just always there on the look-out, protecting and impressive. They're homely.

Deciding to come back to Falkirk had seemed like a snap decision after my husband's tentative suggestion that we give it a try. Within ten minutes I'd been on the phone to my family, rushing and gushing to them before my husband had time for second thoughts. I was ready for this final homecoming and had been for a long time.

My Mam was sitting in her chair just four feet from the enormous telly which her failing eyesight demanded. She struggled to get up as I hugged her frail body, her bony hands patting my hair with infinite tenderness. I was home.

Soutie

Lindsay Scott

Falkirk – 00H01 January 1 2015

Here's tae us, wha's like us, damn few, an' they're a' deid. As the toasts ring
out and the fireworks explode, I feel that dry, dusty heat, the perfume
of the past, slink out of the shadows and surround me. *That's pretty
close to the mark* I think, there really aren't many of us left, which is
surprising, given that most would only be in our early sixties now.
Actually, given the occupation we chose to follow, it's not surprising
at all. Duty bound to throw our wordy weight about, we covered the
globe tracking death and disaster. If it bleeds it leads was the motto,
and in a nutshell that's how we lived. It's also how we died, doing what
we loved best. Ostensibly.

These days, the few of us who are still around keep in touch using
technology we couldn't have dreamt of back then. Late nights babbling
over Skype, reminiscing about the good times – the dreaming country,
where every morning you woke in the streaming, dust-moted light
and, where, during the course of the long southern days, you seldom
sweated, so arid was the air.

Recalling the pissed Private from Potchefstroom ripping open his
tunic to reveal a tattoo that looked like a cross between an ostrich and
a bat. 'I wanted a screaming eagle and what happened? I'm left with
a fucking half-plucked chicken on my chest for the rest of my life!'
Or that bad taste party in the bush outside Windhoek. P. W. Botha,
ridiculous in his homburg and corsage, Richard Nixon, all jowls and
ski-jump nose and Adolf Hitler, impeccable in toothbrush moustache,
armband and jackboots, chatting convivially, drinks in hand, as me
and Arthur Charlton (such an English name for such a Boer) lurched
through the darkness and the camelthorn bushes that threatened to
shred our disguises, white sheets with pointed hoods, dragging a
petrol-soaked wooden cross behind us.

When we eventually got it lit, we saw – scuttling off into the undergrowth like a couple of worried warthogs – two police counter-terrorist officers, one with a pair of night-sight binoculars swinging from his wrist. The bald patch and the tattooed neck told me he was a guy I knew from the Desert Skydiving Club. Not that I had the bottle for jumping out of perfectly good airplanes. I was what they called a social member. The other was a squat barrel of a Suidwester called Eddie Kotze. I'd bumped into him a few years earlier in Pretoria.

The reason I mention him is that I was on Facebook late last night when a Friend Request came in from someone going by the handle "Cave", a name I didn't recognise, with the terse message 'Remember our appointment Soutie'. Now there were only ever two people who called me Soutie. One was Eddie Kotze, and he's definitely dead. Barend was the other – a man I have believed for two decades to be dead too – so this message put the wind up me. The thing is, his last words to me were, 'I'll see you in hell first Soutie,' words which sounded simultaneously like a promise and a threat.

Chalk and cheese. Although we had the same parents, we were as different as two siblings could be. I took after my father, a taciturn, stocky, sandy-haired Scot. Barend got most of his genes from my mother, a willowy, olive-skinned Afrikaner of Huguenot extraction who had met and married my father when he was working in South Africa. They spent a blissful year together in Sasolburg before he was recalled and I was born in a freezing cold Falkirk I hardly had time to get used to before we headed back to warmer climes. I was 10 when Barend popped out in Durban one hot, sticky evening in 1964. Shortly afterwards my mother left with him – I have never found out why – and my Dad decided to quit South Africa for good, returning to Scotland where I completed school and university and embarked on a career in journalism.

We didn't keep in regular touch, just the occasional letter, but I knew he took his rugby seriously and wanted to follow his Afrikaner step-father into the South African Police. In one brusque communication he boasted of almost getting arrested for assaulting what he called a "Kaffir", escaping with a warning, not even a fine. He was still a schoolboy. I replied that I found his terminology and his attitude offensive. Unusually, he called me, obviously intent on taking issue over my last epistle to him. 'Your problem,' he hissed down the line, 'is that you don't understand our culture. That's because you're nothing but a Soutie.' I asked him to explain and he gleefully did. *Soutie* is short for *Soutpiel*, which literally translates as salt prick.

My dilemma apparently was that I was not a genuine South African, having one foot in Scotland and the other in the republic, with my genitals dangling in the sea somewhere in between, hence the derogatory moniker. 'We don't need your type here, Kaffirboeties on the side of the Swart Gevaar. They must be controlled, so don't set foot back here or I'll do something I might regret.' 'For God's sake Barend, I'm your brother...' I started. 'I have no brother.' He rang off and that's where we lost each other.

To some extent, when that happened I kind of lost myself as well, devoting too much time and energy to my work with a fairly prestigious news agency, making myself available for overseas assignments. I was hoping for the hazardous but most turned out to be relatively mundane. Too late for Vietnam and only flirting with East Timor, Cambodia and Afghanistan, I ended up in 1980 watching Salisbury change to Harare to the strains of Bob Marley and the Wailers as Rhodesia became Zimbabwe.

A couple of years later and I decided to follow the thousands of white Rhodesians, many of them with substantial military experience, south to the last bastion of white supremacy on the continent. I'd managed to convince my agency there were better stories to be had there. That's also where my estranged brother was. I had supposed, though never completely consciously, that maybe he missed me as much as I missed him, and perhaps that's really why, at the ripe old age of 30, I found myself in a rundown barn of a room with slow-moving ceiling fans listening to bad country and western and feeling decidedly sick.

Pretoria – 00H01 March 7th 1984

There really isn't a good time to be puking over the green boots of a Koevoet Korporaal, especially when he's surrounded by his mates and other assorted military hard men, drunk and high after a tour "on the border". *If I'm not careful, I'm gonna get the crap kicked out of me on my birthday* I reflected, instantly regretting the double cheeseburger with lashings of ketchup and the two bottle of Amstel I'd downed a couple of hours earlier.

The bar itself, a rough, wide wooden shelf, was crowded with young men throwing down Castles, Lions and Jagermeisters, trying hard to erase either the horror or the tedium of what they'd been through for the weeks before they'd clambered into the old flossie at Ondangwa Air Force Base then a couple of hours later been dumped unceremoniously at Waterkloof. From there it was a short bus ride to Valhalla, the minature city consisting of a big barracks complex and a military hospital amost as massive. I'd been out there a couple of times during the day, doing a bit of background and getting an insight into how the troepies lived on base.

Doors slamming incessantly, semi-naked young men shouting obscenities at each other down the corridors, queuing for showers with towels around their waists as David Kramer's "Hak Hom Blokkies" competed with Joe Dolce's "Shuddap You Face" for their attention on the stereos blaring from their rooms. The steam and the stink of cut price deodorant spreading down the hallways, hugging the ceiling like a cloud of mustard gas in a first world war dugout, as they sang along to one or the other – sometimes it was difficult to know which.

At night, things were a little different. Mostly we skulked in the shadows, dodging half-hearted patrols that got steadily more serious the darker it became, trying to find out more about the secretive arrival of the casualties, the dead and the seriously wounded, from "the Border" and other less well-known theatres of operation, with absolutely no success. Finding this night watch futile, we'd often end up in Die Spens, where, after a shower, the troepies, who had by now changed into casuals, seemed to have headed en masse. It was after all the only nightspot in town with live music, a place literally crawling with military personnel of all ranks and types.

Special forces troopers trying to pick up first year students from the large Afrikaans-medium university just up the road and old hacks, as well as young ones like myself, hanging out in the hope of hearing something that may give us an inkling of what exactly might or might not be happening up on the Namibian-Angolan front. It seemed as though everyone was getting progressively more drunk, maudlin or belligerent, while us journalists racked our increasingly befuddled brains trying to recall which of our war stories we had not already embellished to death and whether there were any more, genuine or not, that we could dredge from the depths of our mangled memories.

'Have a piece of droewors,' was the offer I'd heard. Actually it wan't an offer, it was an order, barked at me by a familiar figure, tall, stick thin and swarthy, in a white, short sleeved shirt and blue denims. Everyone knew him as Die Korporaal, because he was seriously Afrikaans, and was wary of his short fuse and penchant for gratuitous violence. So even though I'd eaten not so long ago, I accepted. *You don't know how they'll react after a few month's bundu-bashing in a Casspir* I thought, gingerly grasping the extended piece of dried sausage that looked, felt and would probably taste a bit like a piece of shit that had been out in the sun for too long.

Reluctantly I raised it to my mouth, desperate not to annoy him. 'Wise move Soutie.' It was the Korporaal's sidekick, Eddie Kotze, who I'd encountered for the first time a few nights previously. 'He won't just fuck you up, he might even shoot you dead the mood he's in – he's got a CZ 9-mil down the back of his pants and a Smith & Wesson. 22 on his ankle,' he cackled in my ear. *I've tasted worse* I thought, nibbling a centimetre from the end of it and trying hard to summon up enough saliva from my dry mouth so that I could swallow and appear as if I was enjoying it at the same time.

I sneaked a glance at the Korporaal and was met with a distinctly expectant look, so I decided to follow the old adage about discretion and valour and started waving the droewors around mouthing 'Not bad, actually, it's very good.' Suddenly something shiny caught the corner of my eye and focussing on the droewors I noticed the light reflecting off the end I hadn't bit into. Holding it up to one of the electric "oil lamps" hanging above the bar I recoiled in horror as I identified a fingernail. By now, the Korporaal and his troepies were in stitches. I couild feel the warm bile rising in my throat as he shouted for the whole bar to hear: 'Everytime I slot a floppie I take a souvenir,' ripping open his shirt to reveal a necklace apparently made up of more fingers and some misshapen lumpy things that could have been ears.

Supper, if you could call it that, spurted out of my mouth, shooting down onto the wooden boards in a warm, wet stream. I could feel my stomach convulsing as I bent over, getting closer to the floor in order to try and minimise the mess – the last thing I wanted was this stinking spray of beer and burger to do too much damage to his pristine pants and green desert boots. I needn't have worried, they had pulled back from me, perhaps anticipating what this lily-livered Engelsman's reaction would be, and were laughing so hard some of them were in tears.

In the coming years, I frequently encountered them, or others of their ilk. At the Oshivelo Gate checkpoint, armed to the teeth and not a proper uniform in sight, tanned and tatooed torsos, rugby shorts, bandanas, shades, the ubiquitous green boots and a definite undercurrent of menace. Or in the mess in fortified, white Oshakati, just off the Casspirs that had trundled in through the dust clouds, "wasted terrs" draped over the external wheel casings like so many sacks of mealie meal under the hot, pale sky, life forces leaching from them to be greedily absorbed into the parched earth. I imagined I could see the dull euphoria of the kill, honed by the alcohol and dagga, shifting into something harder and of a different hue, darker and decidedly more dangerous.

Then in Jamba or Cabinda, as I stumbled through the smoke from the destroyed oil installation at Soyo, just landed by rubber duck, tripping over torched lumps of what looked like cordwood but only a few hours before had been living, young UNITA conscripts. Every time I was to spot the same slightly spaced-out, specialist sureness, serving the ultimate sanction on their unsuspecting opponents. But by then the Korporaal was history. The last time I saw him was at noon on a day of death and disaster.

Ohangwena – 12H01 April 1 1989

Heading due north into the war zone, the dusty waterless expanse that borders Angola known as Owamboland, small kraals, often almost hidden by the man-high millet stalks of the occupants' mahangu fields studded the landscape. Occasionally I would glimpse colourfully clothed women taking turns in pounding the millet into flour to make into porridge over open fires in their cast-iron cooking pots branded "Falkirk". This reminder of home, the legacy of empire and the Industrial Revolution and an illustration of the global influence of the Carron Company, momentarily took my mind away from the task at hand.

But two hours later, Falkirk was well and truly forgotten as the sun glared down on the shambles. For once he was without his green boots. He was also without both his lower legs. Massive blood loss had turned his swarthy face grey and despite the sedatives injected directly into his thigh through his combat fatigues, he was screaming in pain as the medics tried to lift him through the top hatch of his smoking Casspir. Its thick armour had been pierced in several places by RPG missiles and the twisted, scorched interior – floor, seats, and abandoned equipment was splattered with rapidly blackening blood. I presumed this to be the direct result of the spray of shrapnel that had killed Eddie Kotze and two black troopers.

A helicopter gunship was hovering, dodging the occasional incoming round or two, waiting to evacuate him and some other seriously wounded to Ondangwa. As he was hastily hoisted aboard, intravenous lines now dangling loose, I shouted above the din of the rotors 'I'll check you in the hospital'. My brother Barend, determined to the end, mustered some strength from somewhere and roared back, 'I'll see you in hell first, Soutie!'

Munitionette

Lorna Fraser

I hate winter. You'd think after near enough three years working I would be used to it but no, it's a struggle every bleeding morning to get out the house and walk to the works. It's only November 11th, that means months more of this dark trudge. Today I feel even worse than usual. My head's stuffed full of the cold. I caught it from Elsie. She is proper poorly, too ill to come to work.

So that's me walking the first bit on my own. I'll fall in with the other girls going for the early shift soon enough. Probably see Marjorie Sneddon, way my luck's going. That woman wears on my nerves. She always has to be first to hear everything and tell us all about it. Each little bit of gossip, any forthcoming instructions from the management, not to mention whose man might be the latest on the casualty list. What she doesn't know, she just makes up.

Yesterday she was going on about how there's to be some special announcement this morning and that we are all going to be gathered together in the front courtyard to hear it.

Elsie tells me not to bother my backside about Marjorie Sneddon but I could repeat plenty rumours myself about how she comes by all her so-called news.

I've never seen Elsie laid so low. Ma had to come and take Jimmy and Annie over to her house in Bo'ness. Ma says that she's going to enrol them in the Bo'ness Public School. Elsie doesn't want that. I don't blame her. Since she lost Eck at Passchendaele those bairns are all she's got left of him.

Last night Ma said that maybe Elsie should be coming back with her too. But Elsie said that I could look after her and she would be on her feet in a day or so. Ma had crossed her arms over her bosom and said, 'Joan is barely fit to boil a kettle, never mind look after a sick sister.'

Ma has never had much consideration for my abilities. Mind you, Ma has never seen me in a working context. She hates that me and Elsie are munitionettes. I think she still has some fancy idea that our war effort should have been more gentile, maybe working as an auxiliary in one of the convalescent homes. She says she could have got us into Carriden House, looking after the soldiers sent home to recover. That's because she worked there once as a housemaid. She over-estimates her influence.

Anyway we didn't have much choice in the end. It was Falkirk Iron Works for me and Elsie. We'd had to fill in the National Registration and we had got ourselves positions just before Christmas 1915. I suppose Elsie could have pleaded that she had a home and bairns to look after but she wanted to do her bit. She'd said if Eck was fighting then she wanted to make sure she was helping him beat the bloody enemy.

It was the government directing things but I suppose those factory owners were glad of the business. They'd had to change the way the work was laid out for us women, make it simpler. Dilution, it was called. And that meant they could pay us less too.

First job I had was drying off the grenades. Me and this other lassie stood there all day drying and drying. I remember being a wee bit scared, I mean what if they had went off in my face? Well that never happened and we had a laugh while we worked.

Mostly though I've been working on the core making for grenades. What I do is mould the sand and glue the halves together then it get baked hard. It's important to get the core right so that the space inside the wee bomb doesn't get filled with the molten iron.

Elsie works in the machine shop. I would have liked to be placed in there myself. Plenty of electric light and sometimes you get to sit at stools to do your piece. But it's fair noisy and she's gone a wee bit deaf with the work.

It's not so bad now we're into November but it gets hot as Hell in the summer. We have to keep the pace up. Targets to be met. Lately there's not been the same requirement for working overtime. We get our shifts done and that's it.

Marjorie Sneddon started a stooshie back in April when she came marching into the workshop waving the *Falkirk Herald* like a flag.

'See this?' she shouted out, not caring about interrupting the workflow, 'See this? It says that eight thousand munitions workers have been laid off because there's plenty of reserves and that women are no longer needed. It will be us next. We'll all be out of work. We need to take a delegation to the management, get some guarantees.'

A few of her cronies agreed with her but most of us just shrugged our shoulders and got on with the work. Auld Limping Tommie that supervises us said that we should all be glad to get back to our proper place keeping our houses clean for our men. That was a bit rich considering that a fair few women don't have men anymore. As for me, I doubt I will get a husband now. Eck is not exactly the only one from round these parts to fall to his death in the mud and desolation of No-Man's Land.

Sometimes I think about all those weapons we've made and where they end up, the soldiers lobbing their Mills Grenades, the noise of the explosion when it hits its target. I can't exactly talk to Elsie about it. She took her grieving hard when she got notice of losing Eck.

Almost at the gate now, there's Marjorie ahead of me. She's wearing a new hat. I wonder what the announcement will be? We've had so much bad news, lately. Maybe, just maybe they'll tell us this horrible war's finally over. If that's the case, then I'm buying a new hat, even more fancy than Marjories'. I'll get one for Elsie too. Then we will go dancing and do our damn best to be young and hopeful again.

Aisle 10

Karyn Dougan

'Do you have a pound?' he asks, hands searching in his pockets.

Of course, neither of us do. I used my last £1 coin on Friday getting a bus to visit my parents, and I can't remember the last time Graeme had a reason to leave the flat. I look at the trollies that are packed neatly in the trolley bay, waiting for me to choose one of them. All they're asking for is one little pound. You can have it back. We just need to know that you won't steal us.

'There's one over there,' Graeme says, gesturing somewhere over my shoulder.

One trolley isn't parked with the rest. It's been abandoned at the side of the car park.

'I dunno,' I say, looking at it suspiciously. 'It's probably been left there for a reason.'

'Then we'll just need to try and manage with a basket.'

He takes my grimace as permission to grab the trolley. As he starts to wheel it over, the trolley veers to the right of its own accord, bumping into an innocently parked car. I quickly look around, but thankfully it's too wet a day for people to be hovering outside the store. Graeme fights the trolley over to me.

'You saw nothing,' he says.

'Probably a good thing you don't drive.'

'Ah, but I drive you *wild* though.'

I smile and kiss him on the cheek, wishing he would just sit his test and stop arseing about. We navigate the trolley between us as we walk through the automatic doors.

Bing. Welcome shoppers. We promise the cheapest prices around. Sign up for a store card today to make the most of our latest bargains.

We make our way through the fruit and veg section. He suggests getting some baked potatoes for lunch. I know I should try and eat more fresh stuff but it's pretty expensive. To be honest, if I bought it, it would probably sit and rot in the fruit bowl or become some unspeakable mess in the bottom drawer of the fridge. I make a mental tally of the basket so far, our limit firmly at the front of my mind.

Bing. Attention shoppers. Our pre-made salads are on special offer today at only £1. Try our Apple Bleu Pecan, Chicken Caesar, Bacon Spinach, Goats Cheese Walnut. All just £1.

I really need to pull up my trousers but it's hard to look classy hoisting your jeans in public. I can't tell if they're loose because I may have lost weight, or if my fat has risen up and over the sides and is pushing them down. It's most likely the latter. I haven't gone for a run in months. I need new trainers, but seeing as you can't eat shoelaces, it'll need to wait.

I notice a big discount basket at the end of the aisle overloaded with energy saving light bulbs. 'Maybe we should get a couple.'

Bing. Attention shoppers. In aisle two we have an offer on energy saving light bulbs. Help the environment and perhaps cut down on the electric bills that are creeping up and up and making money that little tighter. Energy saving light bulbs in aisle two.

He snorts. 'Yeah, you know how they save energy? By barely lighting the room.'

'Might save on the electric.'

'Fine, all right. Besides, you light up every room you're in so I'm sure we'll be fine.'

I pretend to gag as I reach for a pack and he tickles me in punishment. I laugh but I make sure to suck my stomach in. I don't want him to feel my body jiggle.

'Come on, let's get moving. Want to catch the game, don't we?'

I smile, and think about yet another afternoon stored away in the flat. Perhaps I could raid the "crap jar" and get enough change for a bus to visit my folks.

We turn up into the crisps aisle and my eyes immediately clamp onto a girl looking at pretzels. I start worrying he's noticed her too. It would be hard not to.

Bing. Attention shoppers. In aisle five we have a beautiful brunette. Long dark hair spilling in waves down her back. Slim waist. Clear skin. Her eyeliner is a work of art. Not only that, shoppers, but she has the perfect ass. Treat his eyes today since the rest of the time he has to be satisfied looking at you. Aisle five, ladies and gentlemen.

He's probably looking at her now. Can't blame him. I bet *she* doesn't have to worry about how many pretzels she eats. I bet she's one of those people who orders a box of organic fruit to her flat every week, and grazes on it like some bloody gazelle.

'Hey, you want some?'

He's holding up a big multi-bag of my favourite crisps with a big grin on his face. I shake my head, feeling more aware of my stomach than I ever have.

'Ah, come on, I know you do. A little treat.' He puts them in the basket but I snatch them back out.

'No, no. Honestly. I don't want them.'

'What's wrong?'

'Nothing.'

He looks a little hurt. He rubs his ear but stays quiet.

Bing. Attention shoppers. Also in aisle five you will find a great selection of paranoid thoughts. Distrust, cheating, dissatisfaction. All in aisle five today.

'You want anything from here?' I ask.

'No.'

We walk on in silence.

Down into the chilled drinks. There's a tall blonde browsing the soy.

Bing. Attention shoppers. In aisle nine we have a range of soy milk specifically for those people who exercise, look after themselves and are, in general, a better person than you. Even if you bought this milk, you still would not be as good as them. Please buy your regular full fat savers milk.

He picks up a blue milk and drops it into the basket. (£7. 38)

'Are you ok?'

'Yeah, I'm fine.'

I'm uncomfortably aware of the fat rolling over my jeans. My t-shirt feels too tight around my waist.

Cosmetics, ladies sanitaries and shower products. I grab my usual bottle but I always like having a browse. There's that new shampoo from the advert, the one where the models *swear* it was the shampoo that had made it all possible (not the team of world-famous stylists). It promises to bless you with voluptuous hair. God, I would love my hair to look thicker. Instead I have settle looking like that little girl from The Ring who's just pulled herself out of the well. Sadly one bottle costs as much as an actual haircut so I place my store brand bottle in the trolley. (Another £1. £8. 38).

I stare at the Maybelline and Rimmel stands in the aisles. Maybe I could treat myself to something. I could get some mascara and eyeshadow. Nothing too dramatic, but just enough to look a little more… different.

But as I calculate the prices and the brands start fighting for my attention, I decide that I would need a hell of a lot more than make-up to make a dent.

Bing. Shoppers are reminded that the make-up section in-store cannot work miracles. You are stuck with the face you have. Why not visit our wine section where our cheapest Red can help you forget this. Only £4. 99 for a couple of hours' self-worth – what a bargain!

As I wander back to Graeme, I spot a woman wearing a white tracksuit staring hard at the body spray in her hand. I watch as she takes off the lid, unleashes half the can into the air and walks into the mist, taking a great, deep sniff.

I notice a stern woman who's picking out soap shoot her a disapproving glare.

'Wha'?' the young woman demands. She puts back the spray and picks up a different one, repeating the spray, walk and sniff.

'Jesus,' Graeme mutters. 'What a waster.'

'Graeme…' I warn.

'She should get chucked out. No one does anything about these neddy lassies when they pull this sort of crap. Scrounging bastards.'

I think about the benefits sitting in my bank account and say nothing.

'Sarah, what the hell is the matter?'

'Nothing, ' I snap back. 'Can we just get this done?'

'You were fine like two minutes ago and now you're…'

'What?' I demand.

He walks away.

Bing. Staff call. Domestic in aisle ten. Staff call. Domestic in aisle ten.

I realise I hate his back. I hate how unforgiving it can be. I hate the way it sits in front of me every night in that dark, cold flat. He's supposed to be looking for another freelance gig but instead wastes time reading pretentious wank on the internet, while I vegetate alone in front of the TV, sobbing at Secret Millionaire or shouting in outrage at the winner of the (obviously rigged!) Shed of the Year.

I start shuffling after him with the trolley, apologising to everyone I knock into, trying to keep myself together.

I browse the store-brand shelf in each section. Bread – 75p. (Ignore the cakes. Ignore the cakes). Pasta – 50p. Pasta sauce – £1. Cheese – *how much*?! Pizzas – buy one get one half price, £4. 50. Burgers – £1. 50. Four of the cheapest microwave meals – £4.

When we finally get into line, I do a final re-count of the trolley and am relieved that we're definitely under budget (£27. 98). I look at him but he's flicking through his Facebook timeline. He's probably wishing I was like some of the girls on there. The ones that he knew before I came along.

Bing. Attention shoppers. You can find a whole range of women on our Facebook page. Guaranteed to surprise you by being quirky and spontaneous, about to break into professional photography / dancing / painting and is never crazy, paranoid or insecure. Try our Facebook now and pick up a bargain today!

It's busy. I can hear huffing from people as we all slowly shuffle down the line. The little old dear with her three apples and loaf of bread. Scan, beep, total, shuffle. The short mother trying to keep her three kids under control by bawling at them. Scan, beep, total, shuffle. The older gentleman with a basket full of store brand vodka. Scan, beep, total, shuffle. The youngsters with annoying Australian accents who are draped over each other. Scan, beep, total, shuffle. We are met by a chubby face chewing gum who passes our items through the scan. Beep, total, shuffle.

We abandon the trolley just outside the store and take four bags each, a good excuse to actively avoid not having to hold hands. As we start the walk home, a red-head jogs by us. Not an ounce of fat on her.

'You gonna start your running again?'

He's noticed I've started to put on weight. He wants me to make an effort like her. To be the kind of girl who looks like she doesn't need to run but does it anyway because she *enjoys* it. Well, I'll show him. When the weather gets warmer, I'll be out there every morning.

I shiver, thinking about how much I miss the sun. How in Australia it's actually summer, and they don't have to suffer this dismal winter crap.

I could go. Get some money together and just leave. Leave all of this behind.

Ding. Yes, you could go. Book a flight and disappear into the sunset. Get a job in a cool bar where everyone says "G'day" and go surfing in the afternoons. You'd get thinner. You'd look healthier with a bit of colour. You'd laugh. Meet new people. Fall in love. Live.

But you're scared this really is the best that you deserve. This is as good as it is going to get. You have nothing to offer anyone. Be thankful you have someone that will share your rent.

Yes, you could do it. You should do it.

But you won't.

I just need some time…

Ding. A pile of self-worth has been found by the exit of the store. Please go to customer service if this belongs to you. Thank you.

Rab the Stab

Paul Cowan

Monday morning trickled into my periphery courtesy of a reddish, oblong glow from the bottom of the dilapidated runner door. I could hear boots shuffling about like the feet of emperor penguins, as if the head honcho was controlling them from his office, laughing and snorting like a kid after the consumption of copious amounts of Skittles.

Jammed like marshmallows into the van, the ten of us were shipped from the Graeme Hotel to a world of steel monoliths and paper mountains. BP. A prescription of back stabbing, gutter snipes, confusion and brotherly love awaited us with open arms.

Aghast, I watched Rab the Stab cut his tomatoes with the same knife that had just cut its way through the hard, oily rubber attached to six heavy duty welding cables lying on the van's sodden floor. His chopping board for the now crud-stained tomatoes was an old copy of *Readers' Wives* that had seen more action than Andy McNab. He turned slightly, catching the light, which allowed me to study the contours, grooves and cul-de-sacs of his massive moon-pussed face. If I looked closely enough, I would've found an old mess cabin in there somewhere, wedged solid. I heard that Rab used to be a below-par goalkeeper for a pub team and every time he'd attempted a save, the ball had stuck square into his sniper's dream of a noggin. Clocking me gawking at him, he opened his mouth and it took a few seconds for the signal in his carbon steel brain to send speaking instructions to his lantern jaw.

'Good morning, you finely tuned tadger of a boy,' he said, his face moving around like a bag of frogs in heat, his voice a Weegie-tinged crescendo peppered with his own brand of thuggish bravado. 'Rab, is there a reason you're cutting the tomatoes with a knife that is presently holding enough germs to kill the entire population of Russia?'

'Yes, miniature nuts, there is,' Rab replied. 'I'm cutting my tomatoes in a ghastly fashion on a Monday morning in a van full of numpties, robots and whipper-snappers that haven't even had a sniff of their Nat King! It's because I'm Robert the Stab from Camelon, end of.'

And just like that, the morning connection with Rab ended with him inhaling his two rolls on anthrax into his incinerator like a spanking new Dyson. Rumor has it that Rab was handy with the blade when he was a young gun, kicking around the Brockville club like a slasher with his Tam Shepherd plastic retractable joke knife.

I thought about a programme I'd seen on the telly the other week, where people from around the globe had this overwhelming desire to eat and digest inanimate objects like microwaves, TVs, bikes, doors and the odd double glazed window. I pictured Rab's wife standing in their flat in Camelon screaming 'Do you know how much that couch cost? And you've gone and ate the legs aff it ya fat waster that ye are!' And then she runs out the flat crying, goes to lean on the railings but falls two stories because Rab's munched them in a perverted hunger.

The fab shop roused me from my lethargy. Choruses of bullies hovered around the shop like gangs that plunged their way into working booths and young fragile minds. Fragmented wood-splints bounced from box feet as workers scarred young blood into adulthood; sparks flew from metal munchers and gave the drones a garish foreboding stance; buckled trestles blocked fire escapes, and outside the siren blasted across rooftops and spires to ingrain fear into a dog walker. Inhabitants jammed the wires. *Will she blow? Will she blow?* Cars are abandoned on the wet tar and people stare at the orange burnished sky's dragon-breath.

My head throbbed as I left my swivel chair and walked towards the stores to pick up my tools for the day. On the menu was a 24" stainless-steel pipe repair that had to be completed ASAP, as the 40" pipeline that feeds the North Sea had been shut down at a loss of a million dollars per day. As I approached the stores, Rab the Stab's body language was leaning ever so slightly towards the "sod off" variety, so I slowed my pace and produced a packet of Maynard wine gums to cushion the impact. Everything in the stores came out of

Rab's personal account and in turn belonged solely to him, so anyone asking for tools or equipment was threatening the future of his family security.

'Hullo again, big stuff, have a couple of these bad boys to chew on,' I said, handing him the wine gums. 'Can I have a wire brush?'

'Nane.'

I asked for a chipping hammer.

'Nane.'

I asked for duct tape.

'Nane.'

I asked for a galvanised bucket.

'Oh, wait a minute!... Nane.'

If he says nane again, I'm going to lose my fist into one of his face's deep gullies.

'Rab, do you actually have anything in this store?'

'I've got everything,' he said.

'Give me a balaclava then.'

'Nane.'

The inner coward kicked in and I felt like I was sinking into the little puddle that had formed due to a hole in the corrugated roof.

Half five clock-out seemed like a shrine that I obsessively turned my attention towards. I returned to the fab shop empty handed, cursing Rab's possessive hoarding.

Like a lukewarm shower flowing down a sun-drenched mountain, the gaffer approached and the holiest and most sacred music sang from his vocal chords, fine-tuned by the Buddha himself, to tell me that Jim Devlin had been seconded to the pipe job and I was to work with Scouse Wullie for the day in the heat of the shop. My eyes closed and I kissed a golden alter where Pamela Anderson was playing a harp, donning her infamous red swimsuit. Pink Floyd's 'Wish You Were Here' permeated from the tranny radio I kept in a box beneath my bench, so airborne factory dust didn't clog up its circuits, unlike Rab's brain. The loneliness of a long distance welder can be measured in coffee-stained books and an old battered piece of foam that gets dragged around metal containers in the hope of finding a corner of solitude.

As I clocked out that night, my heart was a slow purr, my body reprieved of the cold tension-sweats that usually cling to me after a ten hour shift in the chemical jungle. Navigating my way around the potholes in the car park, I thought about it never being resurfaced, and left to erode to a sinkhole that would swallow the plant. The welfare of us minions just didn't seem important to the hierarchy.

On the way to my car I spotted The Hogg standing framed by the locker room door. He was smoking his infamous Cuban Havana snooker cue cigar and eying his Harley Davidson, which was parked about 50 feet from any other machine. The beast sparkled like a diamond on black satin and, when fired up, it breathed like a gang leader strutting into an enemy neighborhood.

'How's the Hogg-master doing on a spectacular day like we have today?' I shouted. 'I can see you admiring your gleaming manhood extension. It spends its lonely life in a car park for twelve hours a day! Have you ever wrestled with the idea of taking a day off?'

The Hogg pushed himself from the cabin door and greeted me with the middle finger through a cloud of Cuban smog. 'Some of us have a family to bring up,' he said. 'And what's on your agenda tonight, numb-nuts? Are you lighting the candles around the bath and having a romantic chugathon to yourself?'

'You're a poet Mr Hogg, I'll give you that,' I laughed. I walked over and gave my old time verbal sparring partner a man hug. 'The bromance will have to be put on ice until I chart these waters again, buddy.'

'Before you rush off on your travels, did you hear about our moonfaced friend Rab yesterday morning?' said The Hogg.

'No,' I replied, 'but please fill me in, brother.'

'Well, when The Stab slipped out to the toilet after morning break, Kelvin Conners slipped a crushed up Viagra into his coffee.'

Tears filled my laughing eyes. 'That's mental, man, what happened?'

'The clown had to push himself around the stores on his runner chair so no one would see his boner, the poor nugget. Wee Stephanie also kept popping in to see him – and you know how much Rab fancies the pants off her. His blood flow would've been a raging torrent of lust!'

'Listen, amigo, I must depart as this place is draining my soul,' I said, once my laughter at the vision of Rab's hopelessness had subsided. 'So until next time, my friend.'

I walked towards the Honda and climbed into the scent of old leather. As the engine shook into action, I got a main course of oil and petrol from the air con and was filled with a safe, homely feeling.

Idling over the rough, uneven gravel, I knew I wouldn't be back in this neck of the woods for a while. I was an industrial gypsy, a transient worker with itchy feet and a dwindling bank balance. It was time to earn some real holiday vouchers to exchange for freely-vended vitamin D.

Looking in my rear view mirror, I saw Rab the Stab standing, shaking his head beside his botch job of a Fiat Uno. The bonnet was up and smoke was belching from the engine. Just before my radio drowned out all external noises, I saw him tilt his head back and call the evening sun a 'BLOATED BASTARD!' Before I got lost in the six o'clock traffic, I opened my lunch box, pulled out one of Rab's honking crud tomatoes and fired it into my starving gub.

Poem for Alan Davie

Paul Tonner

catherine wheels reel
across mottled canvas
bright arcs of melody
bolts of harmony
rhythmic pulses
dot dot dot
stars into aboriginal
dream-time skies
reptile brain reacts
to serpentine coils unfurling
among runes cruciforms
shapes ocular peculiar
dark totems godheads
heavy voodoo bass lines
oscillations distortions
deep down vibrations
cosmic scintillations
tribal memory awakened
the bearded shaman
controlled by forces
occult primordial
in a wordless cacophony
of boundless virility
veering careering
brush hand unbound
vigorously now
painting sound
free form
but
now
free from
mortal
constraints

One Nil

Dickson Telfer

When the whistle sounds forty-four thousand boos pollute the Govan
air. I stand transfixed, unable to celebrate with the Shire fraternity as
my brain hasn't yet managed to process what has just happened. I can
see the joy, but it's soundless, drowned out by the prolonged throb of
blue negativity, as if a weight is depressing one of the bass notes on
a keyboard, its thrum being pumped out of hidden speakers under
every Ibrox seat.

I cast my eyes around the stadium, but there are so many of them
and they're so far away, it's hard to pick out any detail, unlike fixtures
at the likes of Cliftonhill, where the expressions of the Albion Rovers
fans can be seen by simply glancing left or right. I manage to clock a
few guys in the nearest section to us though, segregated by red and
white tape and torn-faced stewards. One is roaring at the pitch, face
purple with rage, needles of spittle striking the back of the head of
the woman in front of him. Good job she's wearing a hat. The other
has his hands in the air, mouthing M'ON THEN to a cluster of Shire
fans. Well, I say Shire fans, but they're people I've never seen before.
Doubt they'll be at Peterhead away next month.

When the rage subsides, I can hear the Shire young team sing
'Self Assembly Furniture', a song that confuses many an opposing fan.
During play though, like every other song we sang, it barely travelled
three rows, shot down by pounding drums, the Sandy Jardine second
minute clap, 'We are The People', 'Rule Britannia', Oooooooh
bouncy bouncy bouncy bouncy na-na-na-na-na and so on. The one
I'm most disappointed didn't penetrate though was directly after Andy
Stirling leathered the ball in the net and we all went nuts, care-free
about compromising our voices, screaming to be heard... 'Are you
Stenny in disguise?' But it was like an 80s ghetto blaster competing
with Motorhead's backline.

Andy Stirling's looking up at us, clapping. I raise my hands over
my head, return the gesture and feel my heart pound, like pride is

going to make it burst out of my chest and stain the concrete black and white. I take my phone out my pocket and take a photo of the scoreboard.

RANGERS 0
EAST STIRLINGSHIRE 1

I set it as my wallpaper, turn the phone off and put it in my jacket pocket.

When I get outside, I hang about for a while then buy a coffee from a burger van. Despite it being £1. 20, it tastes like it cost 10p to make, but I sip it gleefully and saunter in the direction of the city. Cans, fag packets, bottles and burger wrappers litter the grass verges on either side of the street, but I hold onto my plastic cup until I come to a bin. When I watch it disappear into the empty liner, I suddenly feel light-headed and have to hold onto it to steady myself, fag ash smearing onto my hands. I take a deep breath and relax my jaw, my temples, my shoulders. I remove a hand and feel my balance return to normal.

Just as I'm about to let go completely, the light changes. I look up to see an angry grey cloud dance across the sky. If it wasn't for the bin, I'd probably be flat on my back. I look back towards Ibrox, the cloud swirling and gyrating as if it's preparing to reach down, tear it from the ground and swallow it whole.

'Y'awrite there, neebur?'

I jolt at the unexpected presence, as if a little invisible fork of lightning has just struck me in the arse.

'Aye,' I say, looking down at the thinning black hair and smiley face of a short, stocky Glaswegian. 'Jist distracted by the sky, ken?'

'You no in the wrang part o town?' he says, not even looking at the sky.

'How d'ye mean?' I let go of the bin.

He points at my scarf. 'This isnae Paisley, neebs, an yees dinnae play The Rangers onymair, mind. They're a diddy team noo.'

'Aye,' I say, forcing a smile. 'Aye... eh... ma brother lives through here an ah hud tae come through tae help him move his, eh, piano.

He's sellin his piano ye see an he did a deal wi the boy tae deliver it, cos he's goat a van, ken, and well... anyway, it wis aw a bit last minute an he phoned jist as ah wis getting ready tae go tae the game, so that's how ah'm here.'

'No the best season yees urr huvin, eh no? But when wis the last time St Mirren *did* huv a good season, know?'

'Aye, it's been a while.'

'...'

'Bit o a crazy sky, int it?'

'That's cos yer close tae Castle Greyskull, neebur,' he laughs, showing his gums.

'Ye talkin aboot Ibrox?' I say, inflecting it like it's a trick question.

'Aye, Castle Greyskull. That's whit folk caw it,' he says, hands out as if it's common knowledge the world over. 'Aw, wait a minute, don't tell me ye're a secret Bluenose?'

'Naw naw, it's jist... well... Castle Greyskull wis a guid place,' I say, mirroring his gesture.

'Ye whit?'

'It wis a guid place. Ah've nevur understood why some folk caw Ibrox Castle Greyskull.'

'Aye, very good, mate.' He shakes his head, an ironic smile on his pitted face.

'Naw, seriously. Did you no watch *He-Man* when ye wur wee? Castle Greyskull wis whaur he goat aw his powers fae. It wis whaur the Sorceress lived, mind? Dae ye no remember him standin in front o it wi his sword in the air an then Cringer turnin intae Battle Cat?' I lift an imaginary sword into the air. 'I haaaave the poweeeeer!'

'Eh... naw, ah mustae missed that wan, mate,' he says, one eyebrow raised, exaggerating the lines in his forehead.

I bring down my imaginary sword, hold onto the bin with one hand and look closer at his face. Give or take a year or two, I had him as being ages with me. Maybe a hard paper round. 'Aye, well ye should check it oot oan YouTube if ye kin. Ye'll see thit Greyskull is the guid place. The bad place is Snake Mountain. Skeletor's gaff.'

'Ah might jist dae that,' he says, unconvinced. 'Look, urr ye share ye're awrite? Yer lookin a bit white there, neebur. An a wee bit sweaty.'

I let go of the bin and wipe my forehead with my sleeve. 'Aye, ah'm fine, jist a bit fatigued fae liftin that piano, that's aw. Thanks though, man, it's true whit they say aboot Glaswegians.'

'Whit's that?'

'Ken, thit they're friendly an helpful an that.'

'Depends whit bit yer in,' he laughs.

'Well, this bit must be awrite. You're awrite. Pity aboot aw the litter though. Nevur seen sae much as this afore. Thur's mair oan the gress than thur is in this bin.'

'Take it ye don't visit yer brother much then?'

I wonder if I should just come clean. Tell him where I've been. Pull the bottom of my scarf out of my jacket and show him the Shire crest. But then he'll wonder why I'm here – in this street – lying about St Mirren.

'Eh… naw. We… eh… we didnae get oan fur a while. Jist recently made up, ken? Long story. Ah did ma bit the day though.'

'It is scummy roond here in bits, neebs' he says, scratchin his neck. 'Ye know, some folk think the litter's cos o the gress.'

'Eh?'

'Aye, cos it's green. Cos Castle Grey… eh, whit did ye caw it again?'

'Snake Mountain.'

He points down the road I've just sauntered up. 'Cos Snake Mountain's jist ower there. Can't be huvin green stuff near it, know?'

'Seriously? Bit the pitch is green!'

'Ah don't know how much truth thur is in it, neebs. It might be God's honest, or it might be pure pish. Ah can't be daein wi either o thae lot anyway, ah'm a Jags man ye see. Don't go though. Too expensive. Apparently that means ah'm no a real fan, but hey ho, at least ah'm no rooked.'

'Ah ken whit ye mean, man. Ah dinnae like forkin oot a fortune either, especially when the game's crap or feenishes nil-nil.'

He narrows his eyes a little. 'You don't sound like ye're fae Paisley, mate. Whaur ye fae originally? Dundee?'

'Eh… Perth,' I say, unsure why I didn't just go with Dundee. 'Moved tae Paisley when ah wis 11 though.'

'Aye, well aw the best fur the rest o the season, mate, ah hope yees stay up.' He puts out a hand.

'Thanks.' I shake his hand and we give each other toothless smiles.

'And ye're definitely awrite?'

'Yeah, honestly, ah'm fine, jist need some water ah think. Thanks again.'

'Okay, aw the best, mate.'

'Same tae yersel.'

As we walk in opposite directions, I look up to the sky. The big, angry cloud has dispersed slightly, casting out an eerie hue. I stop at a paper shop for some water and then continue towards the city centre. Sipping away, I think about the Shire's history. The £10 a week days. Finishing bottom for five years in a row, once with only eight points. The Jeff Connor book *Pointless* where we were referred to as "the worst team in Britain". The pitch invasion after scoring all four goals in a 3-1 victory against Montrose to secure second bottom and retain full league membership. Finishing higher than Stenny one year, then watching them win promotion through the play-offs. People asking me – year after year – if the "other fan" would be taking his dog to the game at the weekend. And now this.

Rangers. On their own turf.

I replay Andy Stirling's goal in my head. The burst of energy down the left wing. The lovely one-two with Paul Quinn. The Rangers defence lost at sea. The onion bag rippling to a backdrop of blue rage. Me going deaf for a few seconds at the explosion of my own celebrations.

Over and over again. Rewind, play, rewind, play, rewind, play, rewind, play, rewind, play. Rangers 0, East Stirlingshire 1. Rangers 0, East Stirlingshire 1. Rangers 0, East Stirlingshire 1.

I glug the water till the bottle's empty and feel a wee bit dizzy again, like as if it was vodka I'd just downed, so I lean on a lamp-post for a bit, grinning, twirling the empty bottle in my hand, wondering what Andy Stirling's doing right now. Who he's talking to. What they're saying to him.

When I finally get to Queen Street, the Falkirk Grahamston train isn't due for another 25 minutes, so I go to the pub for a quick pint. I perch on a stool at a high table with my back to the telly and enjoy the bubbles on my tongue. I pull out my mp3 player, check the volume's at max and stuff the earphones into my ears. As I'm flicking through, deciding what to listen to, someone taps me on the shoulder.

'Ah thought youse did well the day, ma man,' says a tall, muscular guy, his bushy black beard resting on a blue, white and red scarf. 'Dead impressive support youse brought the day anaw, probly bout the same as Kilmarnock. Ah wisnae expectin that. Pure respect to wee clubs like yours, man.'

'Ah don't need yer respect,' I say, pressing play. I watch his unhappy mouth move for a few seconds then close my eyes, but keep my head up. If he hits me, he hits me.

About 15 seconds later, I open my eyes and he's gone. I don't check to see if he's still in the pub. A few folk are looking at me like I'm weird, but I don't care. I don't care about anything today. Except that goal.

I drink my pint then make my way to the train. Fifty minutes later I'm back in Falkirk and heading across the retail park towards Middefield, homeward bound to the loving arms of my wife and the wagging tail of my black and white spaniel.

'Your mum's here,' Fearne says. Spencer weaves in and out of my legs, tail rapping off my legs.

'Whit fur?' I ask. 'Ah see ye, boy, ah see ye.'

'Somethin tae dae wi a cake recipe ye've goat. She wis in the toon an jist thought she'd drop by. She forgot ye wid be at the fitba. How'd ye get oan, by the way?'

'Aye, awright. Hiya, mum,' I shout down the hall.

'Hiya, son.'

'Ah'm jist goin tae the loo. Ah'll be oot in a minute, okay?'

'Okay, dear.'

'Stick the kettle oan will ye, honey? We'll aw hae a cuppa.'

She kisses me on the cheek. 'Yeah, good shout… This way, Spencer, come an help Mummy in the kitchen. Biscuits.'

'How did the Shirey Pirey get oan against Rangers the day then, son?' Mum calls from the living room.

I open the bathroom door. 'Aye, fine.'

I can hear her celebrate, so I turn on the shower, strip off and get in. I wash myself over and over and think about that noise I made when the ball hit the net. And if I'll ever make it again. And I wonder how long I'll spend in here. And how long I'll leave it before I turn on my phone and find out the final score.

Flash Gorton's Leg

Brian McNeill

'Flash? How'd he get the monicker? Well, speaks furr itsel, dis it no? 'Is second name's Gorton. Ye nivver heard o' Flash Gordon, son? Hoo auld urr you? Aye, well… If ye'd ivver seen 'im gaitherin glesses fur Meg ye'd understaun. Whit wi the leg an a' it'd take 'im the best pairt o' twenty meenits tae get roond six tables. Cruel? Naw, canny say it ivver struck me that wey – an onywey, dinny you lecture me aboot cruel, pal! Writin' aboot the wee man in yon raggya paper o' yours, that wid be cruel. Ah'm only tellin ye a' this so's ye'll understaun why ye canny dae it. Mine's a dark rum, by the way.

Thanks, son. Cruel? Naw, nivver… Well, mibby Sammy Thomson, a bit – but that's jist Sammy, an the wee man's eywys been Flash in here, long's ah kin remember. Ah've no the slightest whit 'is real name is, or whaur he bides, or that. He's jist eywys been here, in this bar, widny've been right withoot 'im – hard tae explain tae sumbdy like the likes o' yersel, but ye jist widny've felt right drinkin yer pint withoot hearin Flash hirplin aboot behind ye.

Naeb'dy really kennt 'im, though, that wis the strange thing. Sammy tellt me yince he used tae coort big Jock Harvey's sister, but she threw 'im ower furra docker. Merrit oan tae a Bainsford fella noo, she is… But onywey, ah nivver saw Jock gie Flash the time o' day – no that Jock'd gie onyb'dy onythin, tighter'n a Wee Free's conscience, that yin – 'n maist o' the time Sammy talks pure garbage. If it wis true, Flash nivver let oan.

Fact is, he nivver let very much oan at a'. Quietest wee creature ye saw in yer life. He'd jist staun here at the bar, a' five fitt yinnyim, the thick specs, the short back 'n sides 'n the coat. Nivver saw 'im withoot the coat an a bit tartan scarf. He'd jist staun there, sip-sip-sippin awa at a hauf pint, an ye'd hardly notice 'im till he wis awa, if ye get ma drift. Ye'd be talkin aboot the fitba or the dugs, or haein a bit chaff at Meg, ye'd hear yon leg o' his, thump, scrape, thump, draggin alang the flair, an ye'd ken he wis aff tae pick up the empties.

Minesweepin, McGettigan ca'd it. Furst thing they lernt ye in the Naafi, he said. Gaither a' the leftowers, chuck them intae a pint mug, haud yer nose while ye drink it. Sammy wid shout it oot, announcin it, like. Y'aff oan anither sweep, Flash, Ma Man! Nuthin' but mooth, Sammy, goat tae get'is tuppence worth in tae make 'imsel important. Flash wid jist nod.

Dinny get me wrang, though, son – ah'm no sayin Flash ivver *had* tae drink slops, or onythin like that. Efter he'd stacked the glesses Meg wid eywys pit 'im up anither hauf pint. Said he wis a poor sowel, Meg, felt sorry fur 'im. We a' did, ah'll admit it, whit wi him bein oan the dole fur years, nuthin but yon mis'rable pittance o' a rasp's pension – yon's a bluddy disgrace, whit they expect a man tae live oan, son, ah'm tellin' ye. Man fights fur Queen'n Country'n whit dae they – A rasp? Raspberry ripple, son. Cripple. Nae offence. Jist oor humour.

Ah dinny ken hoo he goat the leg, no exackly. McGettigan asked 'im the yince, an ye kennt right aff that the wee man didny like talkin aboot it. Hill twa-sixty-seeven, he said, Korea. Ivvrybody waited for the rest, but no a word mair. Ye run up it too fast, Flash Ma Man, says Sammy, cheeky wee eejit that he is, but McGettigan shut 'im up quick enough. No as fast as you'da come doon it, Sammy boy, he says. If ye'd been therr in the furst place. Which ye wurny. Whit wi' they terribull flat feet o' yours. Went a' quiet furra while, efter that. Wee Flash jist went aff fur'is empties again. Only time it was ivver mentioned.

So ye've goat the picture, eh? That's the wey it wis, eywys.

So onywey, therr we wurr, last Setturday. Me'n McGettigan, Big Jock, Sammy, Eck Airlie, the hale squad – the Yin O'Clock Gang, Meg cries us. Ye mind the Yin O'Clock Gang, son? Affy the telly? Ye no' mind it? Aye, well…

So McGettigan says wull go an watch the Shire get a cuffin affy East Fife. Deaf'n dumb school versus the blind asylum, says Jock, waste o' money. Man's right, says Eck, 'll be like watchin pent dry. Meg shouts Time Gentlemen, widyez clear the bar. Ah'd clear a path tae hell'n back fur wan kiss o' yer ruby lips, darlin, says Eck. Well ye kin sterrt oan the ither side o' yon Chubb lock, sonny boy, she says, oot. Ivvrybody laughed.

Noo, it's a funny thing, son, but ah canny mind Flash bein therr at a'. A' ah kin mind is staunin at the corner o' Newmairket Street, waitin tae cross ower fur the bus, Jock yappin oan aboot a waste o' money an McGettigan sayin he wid hae nae arguments, we wurr gaun doon tae see the auld Shirey-Pirey. It wis spittin rain, an naeb'dy wid let us ower – ye ken whit like the traffic's like oan a Setturday. Therr wis a bunch o' folks waitin at the ither side.

So ah'm askin Eck furra fag'n he's tellin me tae get ma ain, an a big double decker goes through a puddle'n ah'm lookin' doon at ma feet, soakin they wurr. An then ah hear this awfy scream. Horrible, son – freeze yer bludd, so it wid. Even wi the racket in the street ye kennt it wis real. Ah look up, an therr's this bit lassie across the road, haudin a baby, yellin blue murder – an then ah see anither wean, staunin greetin in the middle o' the road.

Honest tae God, ah near hud a hert attack. Ah heard the brakes, comin doon the hill. Ye could hear frae the sound o' thum that the driver couldnae stoap. Auld Humber Snipe, it wis, green, heavy big beast. Ah wis gaun tae shout oot, but afore ah could ah wis shoved oot the wey.

It wis amazin, son, it really wis – wee Flash wis across that street like a shoat frae a gun. No jist runnin, mind you, sprintin like a champion. Grabs haud o' the wean's airm, dives fur the ither side, knocks anither fella ower. Then the car ahint the Humber smashes intae the back endyit, an suddenly ivvrybody's rushin in, seein if the wean's a' right'n shoutin help ma boab an whaur's the polis, thurr nivver therr when ye need thum.

So we get the wee man up, an the ither boay that took the fa'. McGettigan's gettin the dirt affy Flash, an ah'm staunin lookin at the Humber, thinkin, *ah ken that motor*. Then the driver's door opens, 'n wha gets oot but Fower Faults McCrae, face like a ghost. Oh ho, ah think tae masel, baw's oan the slates noo, right enough. He shoves through the crowd an him'n wee Flash see each ither.

Electric, it wis. The shock atween thum, ah mean – ye coulda run the Christmas lights aff it. Didny matter aboot the noise or the rain or the street or the motors or onyb'dy roond thum. Or onythin else at a'.

It wis jist them twa.

Facin' each ither.

High Noon.

Ye hufty understaun, son, like ah said. Huvye ivver been oan the dole yersel? Naw, ah thocht mibby ye hudny… Flash's whit they cry Long Term Unemployable, cozzy the leg. Gets a bit Sup Ben, or Disability, or whatever they cry it noo, oan toppy the pension. As lang's he signs oan. An McCrae's the boay wha stamps 'is caird ivvry Tuesday moarnin. An a right wee so-an-so he is tae. They cry 'im Fower Faults, frae the showjumpin. Ye get it? Ye no get it? *Cozzy likes tae refuse yer claim.* Ye see the problem noo?

Onywey, it wis ower fast enough. The wean's still greetin fit tae beat the band, till its mither howks it up b'the collar 'n sterrts thumpin the livin daylights oot o' the wee thing. Ye might've goat killt ya wee bizzum wait till your faither gets you hame! Flash grabs her haun. Stoap that, he says, right now. An she did, an a'… Then Flash jist dis an aboot turn, no anither word oot o' 'im, tae McCrae or the rest o' us. Meg wis at the lounge door, an he jist mairched in past her. No even the smell o' a bad leg.

Whit goat the rest o' us, efter, wis that we didny ken'is voice. No a single yinney us. Coulda been a different fella. But we didny think aboot that, then. The woman sterrtit oan at the kid again, McGettigan tellt her tae shut it but she widny, an then me'n him 'n Jock 'n Sammy headed back ower here.

He wis stood at the bar. Meg wis puin 'im a pint, white's a sheet. The sleeve o' 'is coat wis a' torn, 'n he wis bleedin a bit at the elba, but it wisny till ye goat close up that ye could see 'im shakin. Sammy sterrtit tae say somethin daft, as usual, but Meg gi'ed 'im yinnithey looks o' hers. An then Macrae comes in at the back o' us.

It wis daft, really it wis – the perr o' thum, nae size at a', stood at the bar like twa wally dugs. Ye couldnya tellt which yin o' thum wis the worst scared. Macrae clears'is throat.

Ah'd like tae say thank you, Mister Gorton.

Flash jist nodded. Meg pit Flash's pint doon in front o' 'im.

Let me get that, says Macrae, reachin fur 'is pocket.

Ah'm afraid wurr closed, says Meg, ah canny take yer money.

Silence — an ah mean *silence*. Ye ken aboot silence, son? Thurr's different kinds. This yin wis deep an' thick — the kind that lets ye ken ye're oan yer ain an eywys wull be. Naeb'dy even breathed.

Ah think it was the word that did it.

Money.

Aye comes doon tae that, dis it no? A pint, a punna mince, a push bike — disnae maitter which, naneythum come withoot the auld moolah. The spondulicks. The blunt. Whether we like it urrno, son, we're a' jist tryin tae get by in a capitalist world, an someb'dy's goat tae provide the means o' exchange. The readies, the dosh. The rhino. If therr wis ony justice —

Hoo lang did it last? Oh, aye, ah get yer drift. A meenit, mibby twa — a lang time, onywey. It wis Meg that broke it.

'Soan the hoose, anyway. Surr.

Kinna defiant, like, the wey she said it, ah liked that. Tellin Fower Faults he wis a stranger an we wurr faimly, an we'd take care o' oor ain. Macrae gies her a queer look, then lets 'is heid fa'. Furra lang meenit. Then he squares up 'is shooders an clears 'is throat. When he sterrts tae speak, his voice is right slow, right careful.

Ah'll be seein ye, then, Mister Gorton. Next Tuesday. As usual.

He turns tae the rest o' us, nods us aff, yin at a time.

Mister McGettigan. Mister Thomson. Mister Harvey. Mister McDaid.

Then Eck comes in an says the polis urr ootside. Wi'oot anither word, Macrae turns an goes back oot.

Naeb'dy kennt whit tae dae or whit tae say. We jist stood an watched the wee man drink 'is drink. Then Meg went back tae the taps an sterrtit drawin pints fur ivvrybody, an Sammy said mibby it wis fur the best, here we wurr snug in the bar when we coulda been stood oan the terracin wi the wind blawin up oor backsides. We a' sterrtit in oan 'im at the same time. That's awfy, man! Fur Christ's sake, Sammy!

An then ah heard it.

Thump. Scrape. Thump. Scrape . . .

There wis an empty gless oan the bar, an we a' turned roond. He wis hirplin awa fur the back door, the leg draggin ahint 'im, like eywys. Meg burst intae tears.

So that's it, son.' Sbeen a week noo, an naeb'dy's seen hide nor hair o' the wee man. An that's why ye canny pit onythin in yon raggya paper o' yours, 'cos if it a' comes oot –

Truth? Oh, aye, truth… Well, the truth is, son, ye've goat a miracle on yer hauns here, an it's nuthin tae dae wi a wee shy man's leg, gammy or no. Naw, the miracle's a truce in the middle o' a war – a war that's lastit a damn sight langer'n Korea. Them 'n us, son – yin sidey yon broo coonter against the ither. You win, ye get jist enuff tae get ye through. They win, they get tae see ye greet – an if they hud therr wey they'd huv ye fillin in a form for ivvry damn tear. Nae mercy, nae prisoners.

But yince in a while ye get tae No Man's Land, an in No Man's Land sometimes – jist sometimes, mind you – better things happen. D'ye no see? That's why Macrae coonted us aff like thon. Tae tell us that nothin' wid chynge. Tae tell us we wurr witnesses – tae sumbdy daein' the right thing, tae a bit courage buyin a bit decency. Urr you gonny tell me yer truth's better'n that?

So there's nae story, right? If yon raggya paper o' yours prints onythin at a', it'll be fower faults – an' huge yins at that. Macrae's bargain'll be aff. Goat it?

Sae naeb'dy ivver hud a bad leg in this pub, nor ivver will huv – an if ye're still worried aboot yer truth, son, ah'll hae a pint o' it wi ye noo – if you're buyin.

Oh, aye, an a dark rum.'

Eyelashes

Matt Hamilton

I have a total of two hundred and sixteen eyelashes. I counted them all, over a period of four days. The breakdown was forty nine on the bottom left, sixty two on the top left, fifty one on the bottom right and fifty four on the top right. Don't bother adding up to check the total, I did it all morning already.

It took me so long to count because I own nothing to write with and I kept catching sight of my eyes in the little mirror and they always put me off. I also woke up and found an eyelash on the pillow the day after I completed the count of the top right, so I had to start over. I mean it might have come from the top right and thus would have had no effect on my total calculations. But I couldn't risk it. If I had then I'd have been risking my whole accuracy and thus the validity of the exercise in the first place. I'm sure you understand and that the wait wasn't too annoying.

The way I figure it, I have a potential storehouse of wishes amounting to two hundred and nineteen. I may have lost a few since I counted, but I have checked my pillows and clothing, and I figure that even if the odd one or two got away, there might be some new ones sprouting through the skin to replace them anyways. So everything considered, it all averages out.

I don't think I have two hundred and nineteen wishes I want anyways, so I'll be safe for now with what I've got, even allowing for falling out and accidental rubbing. I kind of worry about them all falling out or being burnt out in a fire or something, leaving me wishless. But I reckoned on this a while back, and pulled a few out with a pair of tweezers before I began my count, so I have an emergency supply, should disaster strike and the need for a wish be too great to withstand. It's always better to be prepared.

I don't know if I like having two hundred and sixteen wishes all hanging there around my eyes. I mean people always look at your eyes, so it's a temptation for them. They have their own eyelashes and wishes, but when you can't see your own eyelashes you might forget. Maybe the temptation would be too strong in someone and they would feel an urge to take some extra, just in case.

I wear dark glasses now mostly, just in case.

I have twenty five teeth; Nine on the top and sixteen on the bottom. I realise that you're thinking 'Wow, that's quite an uneven spread,' but I arrive at this point in a historical state, so there's nothing I can do about them now. Forgive me my imbalance. I do retain all the important front ones that are visible when I smile, so you'd really need to be quite interested in me and digging around to find out the whole truth. From your point of view looking at me from the right side in profile, and with me really smiling hard, you might notice a small gap that signals the lost back teeth on my top right side, but I'd really have to be grinning a whole lot, and that happens so rarely that it's hardly worth mentioning.

The lost teeth have been removed, gone rotten or been punched out over such a long period that I have no hope of offering you complete explanations of each site. I forget stuff easily now and I can't recall a lot of them individually.

I lost a whole set before I got these ones. That was nature offering me a second chance at dental completion I think. They fell out all on their own; I didn't need help with any of them.

I made thirteen pounds and sixty pence from the tooth fairy for them. Which I kept. I wasn't convinced that I'd get a whole new set and worried that the potential stream of income might one day falter, so I thought it wise to keep the money safe. Turns out I was partly right, once the second set began to disappear, no-one offered me any money and I was left to manage on the invested original amount.

I used some of that money to buy the dark glasses I mentioned earlier. It seemed like a wise investment to preserve my wishes.

I have five major visible scars on my hands, three right, two left. These include a long arc of a scar the length of my thumbprint on my right hand that renders me particularly susceptible to detection should any crime require the use of fingerprints. That fact always annoyed me.

That thumb one bled so much that I fainted while I watched the blood pumping out of the deep hole where my skin used to be. The most spectacular scar, at first glance, stands in thick white relief on the heel of my right hand and runs about two inches straight across. That bled a lot too, but I didn't faint that time.

The rest are pretty small and insignificant, but worthy of noting in this inventory.

I get brought tablets three times a day. One is always small and bright blue; the other two vary in colour and size: One orange and one white in the morning, one dark red, almost maroon, and one light yellow before they bring my meal in the afternoon. The two night time ones are always orange with little flecks of darker orange through them. I think they are to put me to sleep when my brain won't stop.

There are four nurses that work on my block, and I do know the shift patterns and the names but I won't bore you with the stupid details.

There will only be three tomorrow though.

The one I am sitting on has thirty four teeth; I counted them as I pulled them out. I've piled them on the floor, seventeen tops and seventeen bottoms. He was perfectly symmetrical.

I can't count the eyelashes yet though, not until the blood dries. I'm guessing that he has over two hundred too. That's a whole load of wishes I can have now once I get them all counted.

Maybe I never will. He can't close his eyes anymore and I can't concentrate.

A Beginner's Guide to Romance in the Falkirk District

Aidan Moffat

1. GILCHRIST DRIVE

Oh aye, ye wur terrible fur that when ye wur wee, ye wur eywis runnin away an wanderin off. Ye even used tae go an hide in the supermarket when Ah did the shoppin, still Fine Fare it wis back then, an Ah eywis hud tae git the lassie tae say yer name on the tannoy an tell ye tae come an meet yer Mum it the desk, but Ah hud tae make sure she got yer name right because if she said Adrian instead ay Aidan ye widnae come, ye'd jist sit where ye wur, even though ye kent fine well it wis you she meant. An they aw kent ye in Marks an Spencer's tae, so Ah'd jist lit ye wander off an hide in the wee stock cupboards they hud along the waws, an aw the lassies in the shop kept an eye on ye till Ah wis ready tae go. An Ah mind this wan time when we'd been oot playin in the back garden wih Papa aw day, an Ah took ma eye off ye jist fur a second – an that wis you, ye wur off! Well, we searched ivirywhere fur ye, an we hud the neighbours oot huntin fur ye tae – cus it wis different back then an the neighbours helped ye oot, ken? – an we wur aw walkin the streets, an Ah'd been away up it the park it the high flats, an aw doon along the canal – christ, Ah thought ye couldae drooned! – an Ah wis comin back tae the flat aw distraught an greetin an hysterical when Ah hear the ice cream van's wee song comin up Strachan Street. So Ah thought it wis worth a try tae huv a last look fur ye there, an Ah walk roond tae the van – an there's you standin in the queue! It turned oot ye'd ran ower tae the flats across the road tae see this wee lassie thit ye liked, that wee Gillian, ye wur eywis chasin her aboot. Well, ye'd been playin wih her aw that time an then ye decided ye wanted tae git her a cone when ye heard the icy comin. Ah dinnae ken how ye wur plannin tae pay fur it, mind you, but there ye wur, aw smiles like nuthin hud happened! Well, first Ah wis angry it ye, Ah wis absolutely livid an Ah wis screamin

WHERE'VE YE BEEN! WHERE'VE YE BEEN! – an Ah hink that wis the only time Ah ivir spanked ye, Ah gave ye a right guid slap roond the erse an shouted DON'T YOU EVER DO THAT AGAIN! Ah wis absolutely hysterical, but Ah calmed doon quick right enough an then Ah wis greetin an cuddlin ye, an then wan ay the neighbours in the icy queue bought ye a cone an Ah took ye hame. An Ah thought *Aye, that'll be the last time the wee bugger does that*, but of course it wisnae. Aye, ye wur eywis wanderin off when ye wur wee.

2. BANTASKINE ROAD

Monday 25th August

I got a new Silver Bike. and on school holidays I went to see the new star wars film The EMPIRE Strikes Back with my papa. We went to Blackpool. Gillian went to Spain she has a suntan.

Friday 5th September

Fiona brought in things to class a magnet and a recorder. Gillian showed us her yo-yo. Fionas magnet stuck to the bin and my chair and I played her recorder. Gillians yo–yo is blue and red.

Friday 12th September

It's a stormy day and i am very wet. Scott's ariel fell down off his roof. David is still in hospital he is much better he knitted Gillian a necklace.

Friday 26th September

Today I got a new reeding book it is called. THE BRONZE GIANT Gillians is called The Wonderful Garden. I let Gillian read my book She didnt let me read her book.

Monday 6ᵗʰ October

I got two EMPIRE Strickes Back posters. One of Luke Skywalker and One of Darth Vader's Spaceship. I asked Gillian to play Star wars and be princess Leia She said no.

Monday 20ᵗʰ October

Today David came back to school and he had a operation. My papa is having a operation to. David went to hospital because he fell off his bike he had to have a injection to put him to sleep. Gillian made him a card.

Friday 24ᵗʰ October

Our teacher Mrs Paton is off sick. I usually go to my papas house on a friday but now he is in hospital i will have to stay at home. I went to see my papa on wednesday. He is in ward 10. e.

Wednesday 12ᵗʰ November

It is very very cold. A man came to school and took photographs of us. Some people had them with somebody and some didn't. The man said to Gillian have you got a boyfriend She said no. Then he said are you looking for one she said no. Then he said do you like boys she said no. Then he said do you like me she said yes. Mrs paton is still of i hope she will be back soon.

3. CUMBRAE DRIVE

I think she was my first kiss, or at least my first attempt. We all dogged off school and went to Fiona's house while her Mum was at work, three girls and three boys, all ready for love, or whatever love is when you're nine years old. Each couple took a room and tried to work out what to do. Gillian sat on a bed with me and I asked her: Will you wank with me? But the word was wrong, I didn't know what it meant; I really meant winch, that word the bigger kids used for kiss and adults teased us with – 'Ur ye winchin yet, wee man?' – but I didn't know the difference, and neither did she. There were no tongues, we didn't even know they were part of it, just four callow lips rubbing in rhythm, the way we thought we'd seen in films. And then I ask her: Do you want to see my willy? And she gives me a timid nod, so I get off the bed and stand up – we couldn't have been in the Mum's room, I remember it was just a single bed, not that we needed a double – and I drop my trousers and pants and she stares at me in silence for what seems like ages … but then the doorbell's ringing and someone's shouting 'WHY ARE YOUSE NO AT SCHOOL?' So I pull up my trousers and run downstairs, and I can see the neighbour's angry shadow beyond the front door's bubble-glass, and David and Scott and me all run through the kitchen and into the garden, then jump over a hedge into a lane. And we keep running, we keep *fleeing,* and I'm tucking my shirt in and trying to fasten my belt, and it's such a thrill, such a rush, the three of us all laughing and whooping as we tank it home.

All She Was Worth

Gordon Legge

When friends of Marie first became aware of her being a long-term pal of none other certified national treasure Gideon Gogs, the immediate response was one of, 'What? Gideon? You're kidding me?' Such effusiveness, however, was never long in lasting, with the gasps and gushes soon giving way to the more familiar, 'Has he not got a couple of kids kicking about round here, grown-up kids?' 'He's got that place over The Grange, hasn't he? Just lies there, empty.'

To be honest, these notions, as with any number of them, could've been true, could've been nonsense, Marie wasn't to know; for Marie wasn't one to pry. What she did know, what she could almost certainly in fact guarantee, was that the Gideon she grew up with would be the last person to court any kind of scandal that held the potential to become trouble. In saying that, Marie often used the gossip as an excuse to give Gideon a call; or at least that used to be the case, up until one night when Marie phoned to pass on the latest.

'I hear you're allergic to cats and dogs, household pets? Some kind of condition?'

'Really? Any idea as to the severity of said condition? Whether it's hereditary? Contagious? Potentially life-threatening?'

'No, never said.'

Gideon laughed. 'What is it *you* call them? Airport stories? Bored out their skulls? Tick! Trapped? Tick! Audience? Bullseye! "Oh, Giddy, man, Giddy. That you doing a runner, is it? Caught shagging gangsters' daughters again?" And you try and make light, try and defuse the situation: keep the voice down, "No, listen boys, name's cropped up in another divorce. You'll know who I'm meaning, eh?" Give them the hourglass, point to a paper. Next thing, phones are out, tapping away.'

Marie had heard this before, umpteen times before. Not that that would stop him.

'Or you get the ones just want you to themselves. At you they are, incessant, fixating on the most bizarre, the most esoteric. They don't seem to realise, this is a public place. Or, hold on, maybe they *do* realise, maybe that's the point, maybe they want to draw attention to themselves. And you try and jolly them along, for all the good it does. Rings a bell actually, allergy woman, she…'

'Oh, would have to be a woman…'

Gideon did the voice, the voice from forty years ago. 'Oh,' he said, 'don't you know, women are the worst. No doubting.'

Marie couldn't help but be disappointed when Gideon repeated himself. She called it crap present syndrome: there you go, that's what you deserve. And why did he insist on attributing to her things she'd never said? She'd never once in her life uttered the phrase "airport stories". To be fair, for Gideon to have remembered what he'd said, to who he'd said it and vice versa, he'd probably have had to have taken notes.

But then, half an hour later, Gideon phoned back. 'Marie, darling,' he said, 'go and do me a favour, see when you phone, go and stop telling me what's been said about me. I get it every day. You know what I want? I want to hear about you, Tony, the kids. I want to hear what you've been up to, what you think about things. Know this, I'm worried you're turning into one of these numbskulls that sends me daft links all the time, thinking that that somehow gives them the right to say *I'm their pal*. Listen, I'm not *their pal*, I'm *your pal*. For god's sake, act like a pal, will you.'

It was as though Marie had chanced upon hearing herself as the subject of gossip; and yet she didn't feel insulted or betrayed, there was no urge to go on the defensive or run away and cry. If anything, the overriding emotion was one of relief, massive relief. All she could think to say was, 'You take notes, don't you?'

And that, in effect, was Gideon, he made people feel better about themselves, he turned lives around. Part of the job, he said, whatever the job was these days, Marie wasn't so sure; famous for being famous, she guessed. Gideon never said no, whether taking calls, responding to daft links, meeting this one or that, the man all but thrived on curiousity, effortless charm and never appearing ill-at-ease.

Marie was often asked as to how she came to know Gideon. All she ever said was, 'Oh, way back.' The point was never pressed. Even so, that didn't stop the speculation. Marie and Gideon were both very tall, they must then – obviously – have been attracted to each other. They'd have met on holiday, France, say. They'd have got off with each other, more out of teenage boredom than bodice-ripping passion. Marie, sensible Marie, would've fallen pregnant. And didn't they say Gideon had kids kicking about, grown-up kids, kids he'd nothing to do with? It wasn't as if you were going to ask. Then again, more innocently, hadn't that been the era of the pen pal? Meeting through the pages of teen magazines? An age of secrets?

Even when Gideon turned up for the wedding of Marie's elder daughter – an occasion where guests are nigh-on obliged to approach and interrogate total strangers – even then, it wasn't a problem. All he said was, 'Oldest friend. Dearest friend.' The interrogation Marie wasn't worried about; the wedding becoming The Gideon Show was what concerned her. Along with his ever-present entourage – meet him for coffee and there was still an entourage, the man was never alone – Gideon hit the dancefloor, cheekily mirroring the moves of the most self conscious. He chatted with those he'd met before, picking up old conversations – he must've taken notes, Marie decided, must've – and introduced himself to those he hadn't. Inevitably, he got pestered. The culprit on this occasion being an in law who'd mistaken him for a disgraced former footballer. Even when it was explained who Gideon actually was, the woman ('As ever,' said Marie) would reappear, increasingly drunk, and continue her abysmal tirade. Among Marie's peers, there was the odd grumble: wasn't Gideon just a *bit* stand off-ish, a *bit* up himself? What did they expect? That he'd grant them unlimited access to the contents of his A-list address book? ('My pals are your pals.') That he'd lay on a fleet of luxury limousines, engines running, ready to ferry one and all to the airport, where no less a personage than Branson himself was ready and waiting to pilot the evening guests off to a Caribbean island so sun-kissed and exclusive it wasn't even allowed to appear on any map? ('Then again,' went the gripes, 'isn't he supposed to be having massive gambling debts? That's what I heard, anyway. Not the moneybags they say he is.') Gideon was never going to win. The sweet thing, which Marie wasn't aware of on the night, and only found out about later, was the impression he'd made on the younger crowd, her daughter's generation, particularly the shy, uncomfortable ones. Over the course of the coming months, Marie heard from any number of them. Typically, 'Your friend Gideon's really nice. Made me realise what a fanny I was being. Gave me his number and everything.'

Following the call, Marie resolved to start talking more about herself, and not just with Gideon. The upshot was people became warmer towards her, and were more inclined to include her in their plans and activities. If anything, Marie would have thought it would've been the other way round.

Marie was mulling this over one day, prompted of all things by an invite to 'join the girls paragliding', when she came across a story in the paper. There'd been a terrible car accident. A young woman had died, an artist. Marie knew the name. A couple of years previous, she'd met the girl, and helped her out. The article quoted Gideon: 'Lovely lass. A sad loss.' It seemed he'd helped her, too.

Marie put the paper to one side. Marie had helped the girl because she knew who she was. Gideon would've known as well. He'd have been lying if he said he hadn't.

Marie first met Gideon while she was being detained at Bridgeport House in south Ayrshire, a secure unit for kids such as themselves, kids from small towns – always small towns – who'd committed horrendous crimes. Like their adult counterparts, the kids never spoke of what they'd done, other than to say, whatever happened, it wasn't because of them, it wasn't their fault. The only clues as to their various misdemeanors came during one of their afternoon sessions, when they were given examples to role-play. The examples included: the twelve year old who'd raped his mother and sister; the ten year old who'd attacked his sleeping grandparents with bricks; the eleven year old who'd come perilously close to poisoning his school's water supply; the eight year old arsonist; the seven year old who'd drowned a two year old; the ten year old who'd stabbed a classmate; and the eight year old who'd pushed a younger boy in front of a moving car. The last two being Marie and Gideon.

Marie arrived at Bridgeport in March '69, Gideon a few weeks later. There was no separation of boys and girls, abused and abusers. The rationale being they were going to live in a world of men and women, so they were as well to start getting used to it. The unit was so out of the way that all but the most resolute visitors ceased contact. Eventually, even they stopped.

Marie and Gideon were by far and away the most determined of Bridgeport's residents to knuckle down, do their time and never again fall foul of the justice system. Any problems they had were social. Gideon was withdrawn. Genuinely, he didn't know whether the car that had struck his victim had been approaching or not. Marie, on the other hand, showed no remorse. She wasn't crippled by shame, she said, because she couldn't do anything about what had happened. She felt regret because she'd rather not have ended up at Bridgeport, that was all.

Bridgeport's manager was a learned idiot by the name of Malcolm Gavin. Bridgeport, he said, had 'two primary objectives' – to help residents 'rehabilitate' and to help them 'learn responsibility'. The way he dressed, the boundless energy, Malcolm Gavin could've been straight from the illustrated '70s; blighted and blessed with the zeal of the convert, he was, as he himself put it, airy-fairy to the degree of n. Malcolm Gavin called his afternoon sessions 'introductions – things you can learn from'. Money wasn't a problem. They'd squawk out with saxophones, get down with the spiritual, go creative with the welding gear. The stimulation was relentless. They'd challenge each other's behaviour, swapping identities. A big thing of Malcolm Gavin's was reinventing yourself; if you could do that, see things differently, express yourself, then you could change. Chill out came in the form of Malcolm Gavin's pride and joy, his 27 seat cinema. Their twice weekly (often X-rated) movie nights were followed by appreciation and discussion, before the kids got their nightly servings of what they'd christened journey juice, droperidol-laced orange squash, served, improbably, from a dispensing urn. (Doses of said concoction were given out prior to off-site passes, hence journey juice.)

It's been said, 'a man who for years has endured the cruellest punishment will revolt for a trifle.' For Marie, the trifle was film nights: the aching plots; the distracting geometry; Malcolm Gavin's fawning appraisals, adding depth where none was merited; the constant delayed laughter as if he'd just given birth to a glorious epiphanic afterthought. Marie was a reader, she liked fiction, she liked male-only adventures with characters driven by a sense of duty, of right and wrong, and if at times that right and wrong was blurred or misguided, so much the better. One night, apropos of nothing, Marie kicked off, big time. Malcolm Gavin pushed for an opinion. By way of response, Marie trashed the place. She screamed at Malcolm Gavin: what was he trying to prove?

Nobody attempted to stop Marie. There was no intent to harm herself or others, only fixtures and fittings. Like overtime requests, stock requisitions went unchallenged, even 27 seat cinemas.

When she was done, Malcolm Gavin said, 'So, I take it you didn't like the film then?'

Marie said she didn't, and proceeded to tear into its every aspect with a precision that Malcolm Gavin's morning notes recorded as being 'little short of surgical.'

Marie was excused further screenings. 'Thank fuck,' she said.

(As an adult, Marie wasn't surprised at all to discover that the equally odious/deluded Hitler was also a great fan of having folk round and hosting film nights.)

Marie stuck with her books. She moved onto physics. What she didn't understand, she re-read, highlighting the patterns of words and their frequency. Bridgeport was lively to the point of noisy, blaring music, staff shouting from one end of the unit to the other, but Marie kept on reading. In effect, she taught herself to concentrate.

As they grew older the kids went on passes to foster homes, first overnights, then weekends. Some, not many, returned to their parents. A few bolted. Most returned of their own accord. Only one ever went recorded as missing.

In truth, nothing much happened at Bridgeport. They were kids, they could've slept sixteen hours a day for all anyone cared. Other than chemical, there was no abuse that Marie was aware of. As long as they got their overtime the staff were happy. They'd have shat spiked needles for overtime. Maybe that was Malcolm Gavin's secret – happy staff, successful unit.

Eight years Marie spent at Bridgeport. People had homes for eight years, homes they'd struggle to describe in any great detail. They'd jobs, relationships, marriages, that lasted as long but which were all but dismissed in a few hackneyed phrases. This, Marie tried to convince herself was her equivalent, nothing more.

When she left Bridgeport, Marie enrolled at Leeds University, studying social planning. Between terms, she returned to her foster parents, an elderly couple based in a picturesque village not far from Telford new town. The couple were lovely. Marie later learned that they were paid a small fortune for their troubles.

There was little contact from Marie's birth family. To begin with, she received letters. Then Christmas cards with notes. Then the notes stopped. Then the Christmas cards stopped. At no point was reconciliation ever considered. There was no fuss, no outcry. Any suffering was endured in silence, if it was endured at all.

Despite initial reservations, Marie partied as hard as anybody at Leeds, gorging on its celebrated nightlife and massive student population. But once qualified, she set her sights on working nine to five, and having a husband and family.

She married Tony, a bacteriologist, who never wanted to know about her background, and who to all intents and purposes was as decent a human being as Marie could ever hope to meet.

Gideon, meanwhile, collected degrees like they were going out of fashion. He started with business studies at Keele before moving onto accounting at the LSE. On the side, he helped organise parties, making himself half-way rich in the process, and investing the proceeds in the burgeoning nursing home industry. Gideon maintained contact with Marie. Always fascinated by her take on things, he'd ask what she'd been reading. One day Marie raved about *All She Was Worth*. It wasn't like other crime books, she said, those horrible home counties whodunnits with a cast as likely to be distressed by the vagaries of the weather as they were by the loss of a loved one; nor those hideous hardboiled procedurals headed up by a hard drinking fanny magnet with a touch of the compelling maverick about him. No, she said, this had serious grieving, missing persons and stolen identities. Marie talked her way through the plot, what happened, what might've happened – Marie covered all possibilities and then some – for the best part of forty minutes.

Just under three years later, Marie received an invite to the Leicester Square premier of *Une carte pour l'enfer (All She Was Worth)*. An attached post-it said, 'Be great to see you. Hopefully, it's what you would've wanted.' Gideon was credited as lead actor, co-writer and co-producer. He'd set it in Limoges, although not even locals would've recognised the place, and spoke perfect French throughout, albeit he'd only sixty lines of dialogue to master. At the post-screening Q&A, Gideon was asked why he hadn't set the film in the UK. Pah, he said, home-based films were all landmarks, you couldn't move for landmarks, you couldn't have a blow-job without having to have the camera panning away to the likes of the castle; and as for casting, did every leading man have to have a 28 inch waist, really? Did every leading lady have to be a stick-thin spit of a fourteen year old boy beauty? You've been blessed with this opportunity, this great opportunity, he said, to express, to explore and create, and what do you go and do, you give of yourself a passion and quality that would shame and embarrass the cheapest and shoddiest of lame seaside postcards.

Which, give or take a nuance or two, was pretty much what Marie had come away with during her infamous Bridgeport outburst. When he was asked what had first attracted him to the book, Gideon quoted from Marie's forty minute phone call.

Marie wasn't aware of any of this. She'd thought he was in teacher training. To see him, he was so confident and articulate. And he'd sprouted; a late bloomer, he was taller than Marie. This was a boy who for the first few years Marie knew him was too scared to look at a mirror. And now look at him, posing for the papparazzi, a bona fide star. He must've had everything ready, waiting. For years, Marie thought she was looking out for him. No, she wasn't: he'd picked her. If it was one of Malcolm Gavin's godawful films they'd have cut to a montage of the young Gideon, silent, watchful, and secretly taking notes. The film's big line was, 'It's what she would've wanted.' It appeared half way through then again at its climax. Marie looked at the post-it attached to her invite. The words were underlined.

The film did well – even Marie thought it tolerable (tellingly, no women featured, not really) – but Gideon did better. He'd never intended a follow-up. Had the project failed, he'd have moved on. Every year, he told Marie, without him having to lift a finger, he estimated that *All She Was Worth* would earn him five times the national average wage. And so it proved. Day to day, his job if you like, Gideon took on an almost ambassadorial role, a social commentator, a ridiculously well-informed rent-a-quote. He sat on committees, adding his clout to good causes. He never let up. A big thing of his was how people without any recognisable skill-sets achieved positions of power and influence. To many it seemed that Gideon, being terribly post-modern, was describing himself. Marie thought of Malcolm Gavin, a man she'd never be convinced had the slightest clue as to what he was doing. Marie never dwelt on Bridgeport, it was the barely-remembered home of eight years. She only ever felt unease in the company of certain blokes, friends of Tony's, who, when drinks had been taken, started all that how they'd wished they'd given somebody a good slap or doing, usually somebody they'd encountered on holiday. If only they knew.

Beyond his recent past, there was never any real investigation into Gideon's background. Many claimed to have went to school with him, but no two came from the same place. Some said he was an army brat, others that he was the son of gangsters, others still had it that he was the black sheep of a well-known moneyed family.

Nobody asked Marie about her past either. If it was spoken of at all, childhood was a subject of nostalgia: sweets, toys, television. Of her (admittedly arm's length) social circle, half of them Marie didn't know where they were from, let alone if they'd siblings, or even if their parents were still alive.

Following university, Marie remained in Yorkshire. With Tony, she raised three children, two girls and a boy. Every weekend saw them enjoying family activities, with Marie trying not to think of Malcolm Gavin's 'introductions – things you can learn from'.

Then one day Tony said he'd been offered a position in Edinburgh. Seemingly Marie had expressed a hankering to retire to Scotland. Marie could recall having said no such thing. There it was again: being told she'd said something she hadn't. Gideon was the worst, but he wasn't the only one. Even her newsagent, he'd pick a headline and go, 'Just like you said, Marie…' when she'd said nothing of the sort.

In practical terms moving to Edinburgh made sense. A decent airport. The water – granted, one thing Marie had specified, she wanted to retire near water. At Bridgeport she was five miles from the coast yet never once saw it. In Edinburgh, they could accommodate guests. If they moved it would have to be a city. When it came to small towns, Marie sided with Andy Warhol, the only worthwhile option being to leave. Marie was sure that when she met new people she could tell where they were from purely from the way they behaved.

Gideon, too, had a home in Edinburgh, although he was hardly ever there. On his travels, he'd phone Marie, pretending to be somebody famous. Next thing, the famous person, the real person, would phone, saying, 'Is that that Gideon pretending to be me again?' Everything was the best ever, the best meal, the most beautiful sunset, the most beautiful woman.

He turned up at Marie's for what he called B&B, birthdays and barbecues. Like their phone conversations, they'd talk over each other, one saying this, the other saying that, almost competitive.

Then Marie started the gossip nonsense: 'I hear you've two flats in the New Town, next door to each other. One for you, one for your visitors.'

Strangely, the one thing friends never queried was the name, Gideon's name. Nobody ever said, 'It's not his real name, is it, can't be?'

When they left Bridgeport the kids were given new identities. They got to choose their names. For surnames some of them took staff nicknames. Gideon chose Gogs – for a brief time they'd a receptionist called Gordon, while Marie went for Sibbs – in honour of Christopher Sibbald, the man whose world-weary tones gave them, 'Women are the worst. No doubting.' Gideon also changed his first name, but only once he was well away from the unit. The posh name was so people would think he was from money, and, as he said, money begat money. (His real name incidentally was Malcolm, which Marie considered rather unfortunate.)

When Marie moved to Edinburgh – she didn't take much

convincing – she intended a life of pets and city breaks, family and culture. But then at a Marchmont dinner party she was offered a job, twenty hours a week, a housing officer, maternity cover, a year tops. With Marie's experience she'd be doing them a favour. Feeling pressured, Marie accepted. She kept to twenty hours but the job lasted longer than nine months.

One day Hannah Gavos came in. She was pleasant, if a little anxious. She explained her circumstances. The owner of her flat was selling, and in a rush to do the place up.

Marie said she'd the very thing, a flat in Stockbridge.

No, said Hannah. Not Stockbridge. Her father lived there. Her father was a bad man, Hannah explained, matter-of-factly. He poisoned people.

It wasn't a word you heard every day, poison.

There was a poisoner at Bridgeport, who everybody presumed to be the boy who was never allowed unsupervised in the kitchen. Malcolm Gavin's nickname was Gavos: Gavos because he'd been on one of the early package holidays to Greece.

Hannah could have whatever flat she wanted. From what was available, she chose a three-bedroom ground floor property in Greendykes. Marie had to pull strings, but the deal went through. If Marie had said no, you can't get that, which is what she should've said, and waited and got her another flat in another part of town, Hannah would still be alive. She should have handed the case over. She should never have taken the job in the first place.

Marie was due a call to Gideon. She'd made good her promise never to talk about him. Marie knew what he'd say. He'd quote her, put words in her mouth, something about grief and identity. He was the one who got her to talk about herself. From there, she'd taken interest in others. He'd have known that's what would've happened. The way you dealt with the past was to live in the present.

Marie was the one who never showed remorse. She'd repeatedly stabbed a girl who'd done nothing more than point at Marie and laugh at her for being tall. But this, this was unfair, this had nothing to do with Marie.

All those years on, as long as a lifetime, Marie began to cry.

Under Prospect Hill

Gary Oberg

His torch bleached the weeds along the canal banks bone white. He scanned the beam along the rippling black channel until a gaping tunnel mouth swallowed the light.

'Hey Paddy Wack! Yer batt'ries better no conk oot when we're hauf roads in.'

'Nae worries.' The light found a tiny figure under the high arch. 'It's the Dura-watsit bat'ries fae thae ads. The wans that keep thone pink bunnies bangin.' The girl's face was hidden under a beret and a pink scarf but he could see laughter shining there in those black eyes. 'Cymbals Carol! Bangin cymbals.'

'Okay Paddy.' Carol took his arm in hers and turned to face the tunnel. 'Let's get ghost huntin.'

The torchlight lanced out and penetrated the darkness. Paddy slowly drew the torch up the left wall until it reached the arched roof where a roaring jet of water fell crashing down into the canal.

'The Dark Tunnel!' His echoing voice boomed louder than the waterfall. 'This is the auldest tunnel in Scotland.'

He swept the torch along the arch bolstered by kiln-fired bricks and mortar. 'It wis cut through Prospect hill ower two-hunner years ago when they cawed the canal the Union cause it joined Fawkirk wi Edinburgh. It's haunted wae ghosts o' the workies who died makin it.' Paddy smiled to himself when he felt Carol's hand tighten on his forearm. He lowered the torch beam down across the right wall, on the other side of the canal. 'They say wan Irish navvy goat his heed smashed in oan this very spot, when a rock fell an—'

The spotlight revealed a plastic bin bag floating in the black water. A silhouette of rabid white foam bubbled around the bag.

'Pooh-ee!' Carol squeezed her nose with mitten-clad fingers. 'That reeks, man. Nae wonder the poor dude's ghost's ragin if they slung his boady in a bin-bag steaday burying him.'

'They didnae hae bin bags in 1822 ken.' Paddy muttered testily. He cursed the stupid polluted canal for spoiling his ghost story. 'There'll jist be deid cats in the bloody thing.'

'Patrick Collins!' His name echoed down the tunnel until it vanished into the darkness. Carol sniggered as she tugged at his sleeve. 'Moan then, cat lover. Let's go.'

They walked on. The stark white glare of the torch flitted over house-bricks that were soon replaced by blasted and riven rock walls. Shadows retreated from the light, seeping and pooling into crevices and cracks to transform the honest brown rocks into contorted faces.

'Yeech! That's bowfin!' Carol shrunk away from a patch of light green slime that dribbled down a ragged stone lip. 'The ugly mug is caked wi snot.' She pushed against Paddy until his elbow scraped along the wooden handrail. He hugged Carol, enjoying the intimacy provided by the slimy wall and narrow walkway. Perhaps this wisnae such a bad idea efter aw!

'Did ye ken there ir twa stone faces oan a bridge at the ither end o' the tunnel?'

'Naw!' A frown creased the inch of skin between Carol's beret and her big eyes. 'Really?'

'Aye It's called the Laughin' an Greetin bridge. The face lookin oot tae Edinburgh is aw smiles an that, but the ither face lookin ti the tunnel and Fawkirk is sad and misrable like.'

'How's that?'

'It's a mystery.' Paddy shrugged. 'Some Dickens-time toff reck'd it's cause the Edinburgh way wis easy-peasy, but Fawkirk's way wis a Krypton Factor assault course wi this tunnel an eleven locks fir boats tae get past.'

'Ye ken an awfy lot aboot this stuff.' Carol's eyes were warm and soft. 'Ye'll write a crackin book wan day Paddy, an I'll be wantin a signed wan when you come doon to London fir yir big book deal.'

Damn London! Paddy turned his torch back down the tunnel. Carol had been obsessed about moving to the big city since she went to that Live Aid Concert.

'You okay?' Carol's fingers squeezed his hand.

'Aye fine.' He noticed the white torch glare had leeched the colour from their locked arms so Carol's maroon blazer and his green one were both turned stone grey. Paddy slipped his colourless arm around Carol's back and drew her close. She did not pull away. The Union canal right n'all. He grinned at the darkness. Paddy Wack one, London Tossers nil!

They held onto each other as they pushed on through the shadows. Their ears strained to catch fleeting disembodied voices that drifted up from the stagnant water and down from above, passing through layers of dirt and rock.

'It soonds like somdie's greetin.' Carol whispered. 'Lizzie Morgan?'

'Could be.'

'Go on.' Carol's breath was warm on his cold cheek. 'Tell me again aboot Lizzie and Declan.'

'Whit, again!' Paddy shook his head in mock disgust, and then he shone the torch back along the path they had travelled. 'Lizzie came doon fae Callendar Hoose ev'ry day fir four years while the tunnel wis built. Her maester William Forbes sent her wi scraps fi the high table fir the wirkers, cause it was doon tae him they were aw there. Forbes didnae want ti see the canal fae his big hoose ye see, so he hid the builders go under his estate by cuttin a tunnel richt through Prospect hill till—'

'Aye, cut to the chase, Shakespeare.' Carol broke in. 'Ye ken the bit I like.'

'Forsooth me lady, aye.' Paddy doffed an imaginary cap. 'So anyways, Lizzie brings scran fir the highlanders an Irish navvies, an she takes a fancy tae wan o' the wurkers, ma great-great-great-great-great-great-great granfaether Declan Collins fi County Kildare.'

'Love blossomed uner Prospect hill Ah, Prospect! It's such a romantic, hopeful wurd. 'Carol sighed dreamily. 'The wee Scottish servin lassie an the big Irish gypsy faw madly in love, and—'

'Pross-pekt!' Paddy shone the torch on his trusty pocket dictionary. 'Aha! Definition one, an extensive view of a landscape.' He laughed. 'There's hee-haw romantic aboot this hill Carol? There's nae extensive view in ere, only dirty watter and waws.' He spun his torch around and the questing beam found a white number 300 on the wall.

'Hing oan, this is aboot hauf-wae noo. It happened right here.'

'Sssh!' Carol whispered urgently. 'I heard greetin there fur sure.'

Paddy shone the torch behind them and the shadows at the edge of the light twisted into an apparition in a black veil and inky widow weeds, but only for a moment, and then it was gone. He realised it was only a figment, a mirage in the tunnel. Paddy sighed in relief and turned the torch to shine it forward. The thick blackness retreated from the cone of light, but there was nothing there.

'Pit it oan the watter. Lizzie foon Declan floatin in the canal, ye said.'

Paddy dropped the beam into the canal. There was no blood and fallen rocks sinking into the murk, no burly navvy floating there, staring up into the dark. There were only more anaemic weeds and bags swollen with garbage. *Ah hell! The bloody canal's screwed me again*.

A sudden pressure on his lips startled him. He looked with surprise into shining black eyes. Carol pulled back and gently stroked his face. 'Just think Paddy Wack, if Declan and Lizzie didnae get the gether afore the accident you widnae been born.' She playfully pinched his cheek, 'an who wid ave took me oan a ghost hunt then eh?'

Paddy switched off the torch, and then he was alone with Carol in the absolute darkness. He could not see any ghosts in the gloom, and all he could hear and feel now was Carol's warm breath on his face. He closed his eyes and kissed her, on her cold nose. She tilted her head back and this time he found her lips and he kissed them, romantically, hopefully.

Hopefully romantically!

The words from those lips resounded like an echo in his ears. Love blossomed under Prospect hill.

*

'We've made it past the half way mark now.'

'Oh great.' The muffled voice behind him was loaded with sarcasm. 'This is where poor Declan was killed, eh Paddy!'

Patrick scowled. Carol hadn't called him that in years. She was right though. Paddy Wack and his wacky stories! He didn't need the three-decade-old torch that hung down, unlit in his hand to see the truth of it. There was no ghost in the canal. He looked into the murky green water, and pondered that at least there was no slimy scum or dead cats in there now either, not since the canal was cleaned up by the Millennium links project back in the 90s.

He gazed along the row of rectangular white lights that were spaced out every thirty yards along the tunnel, and thought about how much they had changed the character of his childhood playground. The tunnel was a cathedral nave now with shining halos that cast aside the shadows, splitting the domed vault into rows of black and white arches. This haloed hall was sanitised, sanctified.

He looked back at the woman walking behind him on the narrow walkway. Carol was a wide, black silhouette against a band of light. He realised that he must look the same to her too. They could no longer walk along side by side, holding each other tight, even if they wanted to.

The couples' footsteps and laboured breathing reverberated around the walls as they walked in silent solitude. Patrick felt the oppressive weight of the layers of rock looming heavily above them. He wondered how the walls could bear such a burden and not—

'Will you look at that?' He pointed to the wall beyond the canal. 'It says 480 yards. So whit?'

'No the number, the signs.' He waved a gloved hand at the two green safety signs beneath a light. They had white arrows, pointing left and right. 'That's Health and Safety gone nuts that is.' Patrick sneered. 'Do the cooncil think that we're aw so bloody stupid thit we need arrows showin us how tae go fowards and backwards? Whit other bloody way could we go?'

'Well,' Carol sighed. 'Since they've gied us a choice I'm gawin back.'

'But yir nearly there now. We've jist aboot made it to the end.'

'Naw, there's still miles afore Polmont.' Carol shook her hooded head. All Patrick could see was her black eyes above her scarf, and they were as cold and hard as her voice. 'You go. I'm done.'

There was no point arguing, there never was. Patrick watched in silent frustration as Carol walked back through a band of light. He turned away when she disappeared into a strip of darkness, and his anger vanished with her. Patrick admitted to himself that he had no right to be mad at Carol for leaving. It was a miracle that she had even come this far.

He could see the unbroken darkness ahead beyond a final silver halo. The rock face was ugly in the unrelenting glare of a white light here. The rugged brown face was streaked with white chalk, and rust red fluid dripped down from a deep gash. A wounded clown! Patrick would have laughed if it weren't for the sudden recollection of a teenage girl pressing up against him to get away from the wall. He had told Carol that Declan's head was smashed in, like this poor clown. It was just another one of his stories.

Patrick mused that whatever promises Declan made to Lizzie were all just lies too. The navvy had not died here. He got the servant girl pregnant and then he took off, never to be heard from again. He left Lizzie with his child and his religion. Her family – *ma family*, Patrick reminded himself – took the Collins name and lied about Declan's death to save face. Face!

Patrick stroked the wounded face. The harsh light revealed a scar that had been filled with grey mortar. He ran his finger along the fault, a deep crack that some workman had attempted to patch up. He could feel the rock vibrating as he heard Carol's receding footsteps bouncing back down the tunnel. She would reach the entrance about the same time he left the exit.

There was only darkness beyond the tunnel mouth. Patrick finally switched on the torch and the beam cut along a muddy path lined by tall grass and leafy trees. He headed along the path until the light found a stone bridge across the canal. It was the Laughin an Greetin bridge he had told Carol about when they had first come here so long ago, before, before…

Patrick ran the torch beam along the side of the bridge until he found a keystone with the date 1821, and a stone face below it. The bearded face wore a deep frown and its mouth was turned down in a sad arch. Patrick knew that there was a twin with a different expression on the other side, but that face was not for him to see. He had to turn back.

Patrick turned the torch back to the tunnel below Prospect Hill.

Romance blossomed under Prospect hill! Patrick snorted. He took out his yellow, parchment dictionary and found the folded corner that marked the page for pross-pekt.

'An extensive view of a landscape.' That had been the definition that had mattered to Forbes and his family when they got a hole blasted through a hill so the toffee-noses didn't have to see commoners passing by their estates in dirty canal boats. *Did ye even gie a toss about the navvies who really died so ye could keep yer precious view?*

The last definition of pro-spekt read to 'explore in search of something.' Patrick looked up from the dictionary and smiled sadly at Prospect Hill. He thought of the better prospect of the Laughin face gazing out to affluent Edinburgh, and then the Greetin face staring sadly at the arched tunnel leading back into Falkirk. He was going back along that forlorn path again in search of that *something*, anything that could mortar over the cracks.

'Declan!' He whispered to the tunnel. 'You left Lizzie wi yer sprog and yer god, but at least I'm no running.'

Dodgy Declan two, Paddy Wack one.

Disembodied, ghostly voices welcomed him back into the tunnel. He knew they were just empty echoes. They were only tricks of the acoustics bouncing the sounds of water and footsteps along the scarred tunnel walls and roof, but there was something there in the tunnel.

Patrick peered at a black silhouette in the distance that hovered, framed against an arch of light. It was probably just another tunnel mirage, but maybe, just maybe there was still *something* worth searching for under Prospect hill.

'Okay Paddy.' His voice echoed down the tunnel, passing on through bands of light and darkness. 'Let's get ghost huntin.'

Falkirk
THEN

'The Dear Auld Hame'

An Introduction

Alan Bissett

As the idea for an anthology of Falkirk literature took shape I realised that including only living writers would provide a mere snapshot of an ever-changing town. There exists in Callendar House a repository of old poems – some scribbled on notebooks, some anthologised – lying unseen, undiscussed. Why not include them and display different Falkirks through the ages, giving a contrast and context to the new work?

I made the claim in the first half of this book that Falkirk had been hardly written about before the 1990s. This is only partly true. While it might not have been the case that, before then, Falkirk was being portrayed in fiction and poetry by writers of national significance – such as McCabe, Paisley, Moffat and Legge – a dip into the archives shows amateur scribes through the ages jotting down what was around them, providing those of us in the present with a glittering, historical mosaic, one barely known by almost everyone living in Falkirk now.

I'm not going to make a case for all of these poems being works of neglected genius, set to take their rightful place among Scotland's greatest. All of them do, however, have a certain period charm, or sense of wit, or distinctive voice, or outlook on Falkirk that transports us back into the thoughts and feelings of those who lived here easier than any history book or flickering film can.

The earliest poem recorded by a Falkirk writer is 'Patronus Redux' (or 'Our Protector is Return'd Safe Again') by one Michael Livingstone of Bantaskine from 1682. It is, in the poet's own words, "an Historical Poem containing the Earl of Calender's departure, his stay in England, and the effects therof upon the town of Falkirk; Congratulating his return; and Describing his Virtues; with their Profits communicated unto the said Town".

Unfortunately, this epic 'there and back again' poem is 176 verses long, and so it hasn't been included here. Instead, our Falkirk story begins over a hundred years later, on Saturday 25th August 1787 to be exact, with Scotland's very own bard, **Robert Burns**. Burns was touring Scotland with his friend Willie Nicol and had a habit of penning lines on hotel windows with a diamond-tipped stylus. On their first night in Falkirk, Burns wrote a few lines on the glass of the Cross Keys Hotel in the High Street, asking for women to be treated well, before the pair visited the Carron Iron Works the next day.

Burns arrived at Carron expecting to be shown around this industrial miracle, but it was a Sunday, the Lord's Day, and the porter refused them entry. In a fit of pique Burns retired to the Carron Inn opposite the Works and scribbled his annoyance at the 'jobsworth' onto one of the windows. Carron was to have the last word, however, via **William Benson**, a clerk at the Works, who copied Burns's words down from the window into an order book, then penned a witty, Presbytarian riposte. The exchange is included in this book.

Carron may have had the last word, but Burns had the last laugh, given how heavily his shadow hangs over the Falkirk poets who followed him. Almost all of the inclusions here are written in Scots, in the Bard's own style. **James Black Cameron** follows his amourous lead, dedicating his rumination on life and death to 'Miss Annie Russell, Falkirk'. His pastoral influence is also detectable. Some common, Burnsian settings in these poems include the river Carron, which features in the poetry of **Charles James Finlayson**, **Mary Bowie Gillespie** and **James Brown** and where, it seems, comely ladies are oft apt to dally, picking flowers; the 'sweet wood' of Callendar (**Robert Keir**); and Grangemouth, the 'glories' of which are extolled by **Robert Buchanan**. We even learn from **Gordon William** that the town was 'planned as a garden city / And graced wi' flow'r and tree.' It's hard to imagine this 'garden city', given that most of Grangemouth is now a gigantic, metal labyrinth!

As we will see, historical events are a regular topic for Falkirk poets through the ages: the Battle of Falkirk Muir ('The Highlandmen came down the Hill' by an **Anonymous** writer), the Battle of Tamai (**Wallace Maxwell**'s 'Lines on the Falkirk "Bairns" who Fell at Tamai'), the First World War (**Corporal Dalling**'s 'Camelon in the

Shire', a comic account of homesickness in the trenches), and the Redding Pit Disaster. **Alexander Stewart**'s desolate poem, written in the immediate aftermath of the tragedy, not only records the grief-stricken reaction from the town at the time, but anticipates Adam Stafford's 2012 film *No Hope for Men Below*, which recreates it using the words of Janet Paisley.

Most charming, though, are the thoughtful tributes to Falkirk itself, its people, its drinking dens, its fairs, its schools, even its architecture. Two poems here even celebrate town steeples – one of them by **John Fleming** about the main Steeple in the High Street, a second written by another **Anonymous** scribe, from the watchful point of view of Bo'ness Steeple – symbols perhaps of the changing times. Fleming echoes some of the sentiments from our contemporary writers – that Falkirk is changing too quickly, losing its hold on the past – although he seems rather more excited about it than our current crop do, sensing 'improvement' rather than corporate homogenisation. No longer will people have to squeeze into buildings as tram cars hurtle past! claims Fleming. Quaint, and proof that change is a constant. All the more reason for poets to record it.

There is an unfortunate dearth of female poets to be found in the archives, Mary Gillespie being our sole representative. Perhaps this is indicative of the times, but nonetheless, it would've been interesting to us in the present day to experience Falkirk's changes through the eyes of women as well as men. Two writers in particular seem to dominate, in this respect: Robert Buchanan, who barely seems to miss a chance to deliver a public homily to Falkirk's inhabitants – whether part of a Burns Centenary or at Hogmanay – and **John A. Thomson**, whose poems about drunken nights in bars, laddish banter and Falkirk's footballing chances seem to directly prefigure Gordon Legge's novels from the 1990s.

Throughout the years, the *Falkirk Herald* seems to have been a staunch publisher of local poetry.

Biographical details for these writers are patchy, but fascinating where they do exist, some of them telling of the terrors of the Industrial Age. In 1848, James Black Cameron's right arm was mangled by machinery at the Vulcan Foundry, Port Dundas, and had to be amputated. He was only fourteen. John Fleming lost his sight in an explosion at Redding, Polmont, in 1906. Literature turned out to be the lifeline to which both of these men clung.

Mary Bowie Gillespie was a teacher at Denny Public School, before becoming headmistress of a school in Perthshire, then studying for an L. L. A. (Lady Literate in Arts) at the University of St Andrews. She returned to Denny in 1888, at the age of 34, to be a newspaper columnist and poet; all in all, remarkable achievements for a woman of her era.

In a similar spirit, James Brown survived an impoverished childhood to gain Science certificates, through night-classes which he had to attend in the evening, after mining shifts near Slamannan. Wallace Maxwell also worked in coal, though in a more clerical capacity, for the Callendar Company and the gigantically-named 'Messrs Russell and Son of Blackbraes and Boghead Collieries and Almond Ironworks', before winning the Falkirk Burns Anniversary Competition in 1887 and the Burns Centenary Competition in 1896.

It is, however, the irrepressible Robert Buchanan who by some distance appears to be the most significant of Falkirk's writers in the 19th Century, so much so that a monument was erected to him in 1899. I have only included three of his poems here, but I would advise readers to seek out the collection *Poems, Songs and OtherWritings by Robert Buchanan, Falkirk* edited by James Love in 1901 (a copy exists in the Falkirk Archives, Callendar House, but the website electricscotland. com also brings up an online edition). Physically weak, Buchanan shunned manual labour for education and music, becoming a fine singer and flute player, and eventually a Customs Officer at the port of Grangemouth, a place for which he had great affection. He was also a prolific correspondent to the town for the *Falkirk Herald*, and his best works addressed his own local area. Buchanan eventually penned in 1865 what became the closest Falkirk has ever had to a recognised anthem, 'The Dear Auld Hame'.

Their life stories make me proud to be from Falkirk. What emerges from these biographical snapshots is a questing self-improvement, a determination from each writer to overcome tremendous odds – of gender, of poverty, of physical disability – to make their mark on the pages of history, using the sheer power of the written word.

I am delighted to confirm with their inclusion in this volume that all of them have achieved this.

Lines at Falkirk

Robert Burns, 1787

Sound be his sleep, and blythe his morn,
That never did a lassie wrang, -
Who poverty ne'er held in scorn. -
For misery ever tholed a pang.

Lines at Carron

Robert Burns, 1787

We cam' na ere to view your warks
In hopes to be mair wise,
But only, lest we gang to hell,
It may be nae surprise:
But when we tirled at your door,
Your porter dought na hear us;
Sae may, should we to hell yett come,
Your billy Satan sair us.

Reply to Robert Burns

William Benson, 1787

If you came here to view our works
You should have been more civil
Than to give a fictitious name,
In hopes to cheat the devil,
Six days a week to you and all,
We think it very well;
The other if you go to church,
May keep you out of hell.

Sweet Wood of Callendar

Robert Keir, 1827

I like the twinkle o' your e'e,
Sweet lassie will ye gang wi' me,
And spend the cannie time awee.
In yon sweet wood of Callendar.
The hazel grows, the primrose blows.
The birdies sing, the echoes ring.
The leaves are green, fair to be seen,
In yon sweet wood of Callendar.

How saftly blaws the western breeze!
How sweetly hum the little bees!
How bright the sun blinks on the trees!
In yon sweet wood of Callendar.
The present hour is in our power,
In youthful prime, then seize on time,
Since life's a day, let us be gay,
In yon sweet wood of Callendar.

What transport does the season bring!
Like youth, so lovely is the spring;
Then come and hear the mavis sing.
In yon sweet wood of Callendar.
If you'll agree to gang wi' me,
I'll often stand, and press your hand.
And prie your mou', my bonnie dou.
In yon sweet wood of Callendar.

This poem appeared in the first issue of the Falkirk Monthly Magazine. *It was probably written by Robert Keir, the editor, or by his father Peter Kier, clockmaker. When originally published, it was preceded by the following notes: "Callendar Wood, during the life of the late proprietor, was the favourite retreat of lovers. Under the oak or birken tree, concealed from every eye, they breathed their tender tales of love; while, 'The flowers did vie in all their charms the hour of heaven to grace.'"*

A New Year's Sang for Fa'kirk

Robert Buchanan, 1857

Around the ingle bleezing bright,
Wi' twa three cronies dear,
We gather on this happy night,
To welcome in the year.
Anither year o' toil and care,
Sair fechts for right or wrang,
Wi' blinks o' sunshine here and there
To cheer the road we gang.

As round our merry circle flows
The laugh, the sang, the jest,
Care flees awhile, and sorrow goes
Unbidden frae each breast.
Joy sits supreme on every cheek,
Hope keeks frae ilka e'e;
Prudence is by, but winna speak –
She weel can wait a wee.

Noo, cries friend Tam, a bumper fill;
Come, mak yoursels at hame,
And pledge me a' wi' right guidwill,
The toast I'm gaun to name.
It winna be the auld sang ower,
To nobles or a croon;
But here's success, and wealth, and power,
To dear auld Fa'kirk Toon.

To dear auld Fa'kirk – may she soar
Aboon Time's nipping hand,
While ilk year sees her more and more
An honour to our land.

Her institutions, may they rise,
And bring to age and youth
That glorious light, which never dies,
Of Wisdom and of Truth.

Success to ilka ane wha rules
Her council and her laws,
And ill luck seize the silly fools
Wha wad disown her cause.
Sae to your feet, lads, send it doon
Wi' a rattling, roaring cheer –
Lang life and health to Fa'kirk Toon,
And a happy, blyth New Year.

First published in the Falkirk Herald, *December 31, 1857.*

Address to Fa'kirk

[After the Celebration of the Burns Centenary]

Robert Buchanan, 1859

Auld Fa'kirk, honour to thy name,
Wide spread the pinions o' thy fame
Ower a' the warl', like ony flame,
When nichts are blawy;
And sorrow come, and muckle shame,
On them that ca' ye.

Though frosty noo thy pow and auld,
Thy haffets wearin' thin and cauld,
And just a thocht less crouse and bauld,
As in gane days,
There's warm hearts within your fauld
To sing thy praise.

Lang hae ye warstled wi' the warl',
And often stood its angry snarl;
Yet richt ne'er at your heart did dirl,
Nor waited lang,
Till a' your pith o' sense ye'd hurl
Upon the wrang.

Hoo mony changes hae ye seen
Sin' first upon this shifting scene
Ye raised yer heid fu' braw and bien
Upon the muir?
And, keeking round wi' sturdy mien,
Said, "Bide ye there."

Ye saw the time when Wallace wicht,
Flang owre his plaid and grippit ticht
His big braidsword, whose very sicht
Wad mak ye trum'le;
And strove to crush oppression's micht,
And tyrants hum'le.

And on that day, the bluidy day,
When puir auld Scotia stood at bay,
And gallant Graeme and mony mae
Death's portion shared –
Ye saw them laid amang the clay
I' your auld kirk-yaird

And there they sleep, nae mair to feel
Upon their necks the tyrant's heel –
But yet their spirits, brave and leal,
Remain amang
Auld Scotia's sons, as true as steel,
Where'er they gang.

In every clime, in every land –
Whare'er o' Scotia's sons a band
Can grup ilk ither by the hand
Wi' friendly nod,
Then hills and mountains winna stand
Upon their road.

And when on some far distant shore,
Amid the deadly battle's roar,
Inspir'd by glorious deeds of yore,
They draw their swords,
Then, charging, make terrific splore
'Mang craven hordes

Or see them scale the grisly hicht,
Whaur freedom's foes in countless micht
Sends death amang them, left and richt,
Wi' murderous skill;
Yet aye their cry, clear, ringin', bricht,
Is onward still!

But ANE has sung this glorious strain
In lines, whose lustre ne'er shall wane
As lang's the gowden sun shall reign
Ower earthly scene;
Yer trusty " bairns" will aiblins ken
The BARD I mean.

He was a noble-hearted chiel,
An' loved auld Scotia dear an' weel,
An' sung her sangs wi' sturdy zeal,
Nor fash'd his thoom
Hoo folk, to wham sycophants kneel,
Micht glunch and gloom.

He had his fauts, I dinna doot them;
But are there ony folk without them?
Though some there are wha try to clout them
Wi' holy grins.
But rive the rags frae roun' about them,
Then view their sins.

Lord! had he been alive the noo,
And ony o' the slandering crew
Just even daured to ope a mou'
Against his fame,
His satire shafts wad pierced them through
And show'd their shame

But weel they ken that Rab, puir man,
Can ne'er review his ain auld Ian',
And sae they hurl, curse, and ban'
Upon his heid;
And wi' a' hellish arts they can
Insult the deid.

Oh, noble Burns! had I thy power,
I'd scourge the hounds frae door to door,
And drive them to some barren moor,
Whaur their dreed howls
Micht wauk auld Nick in some dark hour
To claim their souls.

And Fa'kirk, ye have lived and seen
A' this, and muckle mair, I ween;
And aften tears have dimmed your een
Wi' grief and shame,
To hear sic trash, no worth a preen,
Traduce his name.

But there is ane within your toon
Shall tentie watch when ony loon
May cater ill, or ca' Rab doon –
Then redd the road,
He'll tak their length wi' broken croon
Upon the sod.

Lang live his honest thinking heart –
May Fa'kirk aye can claim a part
O' his strong arm, and every art
That he can wield,
Pierce Robert's foes like ony dart,
Till ance they yield.

Weel did he earn the laurelled chair
That nicht when a' thy "bairns" were there,
And offer up their kindly prayer
To kindly heaven, And thanks that Rab, a gem sae rare,
To us was given.

And what sweet streams o' pure delight
Gushed forth on that ae happy night,
Ages and ages yet shall write,
And glory shine
On a' that laid their wee bit mite
At Robert's shrine.

My dear auld toon, I'm unco prood
To see thy name among the crood
That paid just tribute to the good
Immortal bard,
May virtue's ever honour'd snood
Be your reward.

And sae, fareweel, but ere I gang,
May every earthly blessing lang
Creep roun' about and keep frae wrang
Thine honour'd wa's,
And may ye rear braw sons o' sang
To sing your cause.

Success to him* wha rules the roast,
Lang may his tongue wag owre a toast,
And pledge again auld Scotia's boast
Wi' three times three;
Speak out, man, Tam, ne'er mind the cost,
Gin richt you be.

* Provost Thomas Kier.

This poem was first published in the Falkirk Herald *of February 10th, 1859, after a convivial gathering at the Red Lion Hotel on January 25th, 1859.*

Grangemouth Glories – No. II

Robert Buchanan, 1864

Come gather, gather, boys, and sing the glorious joys
Of a day that old and young will long remember, O;
"When the people of the Port came out to see the sport"
On the famous twenty-seventh of September, O.

Aurora far and high, when she smelt the monstre pie
That was baking hot by Meikle,* nice and handy, O,
Said, "Now I'll don my best ('tis by special request),
And appear in golden colours quite the dandy, O."

Then the birds in chorus sang, and the woods with music rang,
And the streamlets tripped their windings, featly dancing, O;
And the waves upon the sea kicked up their heels so free,
Like a regiment of moss-troopers gaily prancing, O.

From truck to deck the ships were clad with spangled strips
That fluttered'mongst the zephyrs of the morning, O,
And the glisten of their sheen added glory to the scene,
And banished worldly troubles without warning, O.

In gay and smiling ranks, all along the verdant banks
Of the deep, unruffled, flowing River Carron, O,
There were lilies of the valleys, and Sallys from our alleys,
Queens of Sheba and fair roses of old Sharon, O.

But now the sports begun. Hark! there's M'Culloch's** gun,
Watt and Aitken's at their station tight and handy, O;
While Kelly's*** ready by, with the whole thing in his eye –
He's the boy, you'll all admit, that's worth his candy, O.

M'Culloch's gun again – now they're off all might and main,
Like the witches wildly chasing Tam o' Shanter, O;
Bearing round the starboard tack – amid thundering cheers
they're back, "Caller Ou'" winning gamely in a canter, O.

O'twas a glorious day, and the park in grand array
An Eden of the fairest flowers resembled, O,
That ne'er was'neath the sun, "I'll bet ten pounds to one,"
Such a galaxy of beauteous girls assembled, O.

There were Misses S. and C. , and the lovely Misses T. ,
And a host of peerless beauties smiling sweetly, O;
Mrs. Grundy sure herself – the old, crusty, meddling elf –
Would for once have vowed they'd all behave discreetly, O.

And far beyond compeer, there was princely Provost Kier,
With the genial heart of Newton Mains, brave Sandy, O;
They're kings o' trumps them both, and if you're nothing loth,
Why, we'll drink their healths in nothing else than brandy, O.

But again begins the fun, and round the ring they run,
While the cheering woke the echoes of old panson, O;
And olden hearts were warmed, and younger ones were
charmed with the leaping, tossing, vaulting, and the dancing, O.

O'twas a gorgeous day, but at last it passed away,
'Mid the burnished clouds of dazzling golden glory, O;
But ne'er while time goes by will its remembrance die,
But will live enthroned, immortal in fame's story, O.

* Baker in Grangemouth, and famous for his pies. His shop was a favourite
resort of young men on Saturday evenings.
** Captain M'Culloch, who officiated as Commodore and started the boats.
*** Mr. James Kelly, to whose labours much of the success of the gathering
was due.

This piece appeared in the Falkirk Herald *of October 1ˢᵗ, 1864, under the nom de
plume of "IVANHOE". The occasion was the revival, after a lapse of thirteen years, of
the rowing matches and Scottish Games at Grangemouth. Buchanan was describing
these events as local correspondent for the* Herald.

Petition of Bo'ness Steeple to the Inhabitants

Anonymous, c. 1865

I have come before you, honest people.
A plain substantial upright Steeple
Trusting that pitty on ane gaud hae
As all I ask is the time a' day
Some folks do need a cloak to hide
The mony faults that ills betide
But what I ask is a clock to guide
The thoutless as through life they slide
And tell to man as time flies past
That on my dial is marked his last
The young will see how time does fly
The aged learn that they must die
The man of honest industry I'll chur
The midnight thief I'll find with fear
A useful friend I thus will be
Kind folks if ye subscribe for me
For live it is a sad disgrace
To face the world without a face
How thus absurdly I do look
Think I connected wi' a Duke
You've put on me a coat of Arms
To please the Nobles and the Bairns
But use of Arms without a hand
Is ill for me to understand
Even Lithgow pair as Lazarus sel'
Hae gotten baith a clock and Bell
And douce auld Courous ower the sea
Does often tinkilly chime at me
In truth it's truly real provoking

Kind folks I pray thee gang a blocking
And try if ye can siller hatch
That I wi other Steeples match
Is all I ask you honest people

Yours
Bo'ness Steeple

This poem can be viewed as part of the Bo'ness Town Clerk/Bo'ness Town Council/Local Authorities Group at A005. 023/05 in the Falkirk Archives, Callendar House.

Dedicated to Miss Annie Russell, Falkirk

James Black Cameron, 1877

I. BIRTHS.

WE bind ourselves to life with wreaths of flowers;
Buds of fair promise blossom in the spring,
And childish voices visit us, and bring
Back the remembrance of our childhood's hours,
Vivid and fresh as in a morning-dream;
And little arms around our necks are twined,
And soft cheeks pressed to ours, till we grow blind
To all, save the fair promises, which seem
To gild the future, as in recompense
For sorrows past. And surely it is wise
To look oft times at earth through childhood's eyes,
And feel within us its unhackneyed sense
Of credulous enjoyment, and its quick relapse
Into contentment, after life's mishaps.

II. MARRIAGES.

We bind ourselves to life with wreaths of flowers,
Odorous with love and rainbow-dyed with hope;
We consecrate a dome of amplest scope
Wherein to treasure up all that is ours —
Sweetest and dearest — and we call it home,
And in it place what fancy fondly deems
A true divinity — and yet of clay:
And well if this opinion lasts for aye,
And time serves not to disenchant our dreams.
It needs must be that cares and griefs will come,

And sorrow's cloud above our pathway lower:
Let love and trust but brighten – and behold
The darkness turned to light!
That sun has power
To flush the blackest vapour o'er with gold.

III. DEATHS.

We bind ourselves to life with wreaths of flowers,
But summer passes and the autumn comes –
The heart's-ease petals fall; the purple blooms
Fade from love's roses, and the trusted powers

Of friendship fail with the forget-me-not.
But death binds us to him. Day after day
Some cherished part of us doth pass away,
No more to be, but ne'er to be forgot!
So we die daily. So doth death become
Not grim and stern, but a most kindly host,
And his dim, silent land our wished-for home,
Where dwell our dearest ones – not lost – not lost-
But only waiting till this dream be o'er,
To meet and greet us on the tranquil shore!

First published in Cameron, James Black (1877), Poems and Songs, *William P. Nimmo (London & Edinburgh)*

School Song

Anonymous, 1884

Sung to the tune of 'Fine old English Gentleman'.

There was a fine old school of yore with a fine old draughty "Gym"
And it had a fine Headmaster with a fine old length of limb,
And a lot of fine old pupils and fine old masters too
And a fine old sergeant, with a coat of fine old scarlet hue.

Chorus – Like a fine old Blairlodge gentleman, One of the olden time.

And it had a fine old cricket ground with a fine old cricket tent,
That let in all the fine old rain through every fine old rent.
Till at last the fine old pupils thought they'd finely like to try
The fine old new Pavilion that was coming – by and by,

Chorus

And it had a fine old football field with a fine old set of drains,
That kept its fine old turf so free from our fine old Scottish rains,
That a fine old joke went circling round, of fine old humour grim,
That it really wasn't safe to play if you hadn't learnt to swim,

Chorus

And a fine old sight it was to see, in a fine old football match,
The fine old quarters chuck the ball for the fine old halves to catch,
And the fine old halves fly like the wind straight through opposing host!
And land at last the fine old ball between the fine old posts.

Chorus

And it had a fine Society, which in casual debates
Would overthrow great governments or disenfranchise states,
And when its fine old President found things a trifle flat,
He said, "My fine old members, we must use the fine old hat"

Chorus

And it had a fine old Captain who played the fine old game
Of cricket in a fine old way that gained him world-wide fame.
And he spent his holidays in France until he got the hang
Of the fine old Gallic lingo with its fine old nasal twang.

Chorus

And its first two fine old Prefects, Bobby S. and Billy Holms,
They fudged a lot of fine old facts from fine old fusty tomes.
And attacked the fine old questions with such a fine old twist.
That they gained two fine old places in the fine old Woolwich list.

Chorus

And it had a fine old baker in a fine old brimless hat.
Which cost a fine old groat perhaps (and very dear at that);
His fine old love-locks would have made a dozen fine old wigs;
He was always baking fine old rolls, or feeding fine old pigs.

Chorus

He wore a fine old flannel shirt (for coat and vest had gone).
And but one fine old brace to hang his fine old trousers on,
And a fine old dim tradition said – but please remark 'twas dim –
That if you scraped off flour enough, at last you'd come to him.

Chorus

And here's a fine old health to all, and not to keep you long,
I'm going to make a fine old end unto this fine old song –
Let every fine old Blairlodge boy stick to the fine old rule
Of keeping up the fine old fame of fine old Blairlodge School.

The song was printed in the Blairlodge School magazine of Christmas 1884.
The school occupied the extended premises which now house H. M. Institution,
Polmont.

Lines on the Falkirk 'Bairns' who Fell at Tamai

Wallace Maxwell, c. 1897

Oh, war! thou offspring of a fallen world,
Another host of victims thou hast found;
Thy flag, on Egypt's sandy plains unfurled,
Waves o'er a patriot band with honours crowned.

The palm of victory has been dearly bought,
And shouts of triumph drowned the parting sigh
Of noble hearts, who for their country fought
And shed their blood at fatal Tamai.

And well has Scotland for this victory paid,
While Falkirk o'er her sons heaves many a sigh,
Though laurels such as theirs can never fade,
For died they not as soldiers wish to die?

Yes, though to many a home the victory brings
Sorrow for sons who will return no more,
A cloud of glory round their memory clings,
And sheds its lustre on old Scotia's shore.

For when, at duty's call, did Scotland fail
To lead to victory her Highland band?
Or how can earthly power hope to prevail
O'er Freedom's sons from an unconquered land?

Yes, Falkirk well may feel a thrill of pride
Mingle with sorrow for brave Aitken's fall;
While for the six who now lie side by side
The British flag was not too good a pall.

So when returning peace with triumph brings
The Forty-second to their native shore,
Remember those whose fondest memory clings
Round brave young sons who will return no more.

First published in Harvey,William (ed. , 1897), The Harp of Stirlingshire,
J. and R. Parlane (Paisley).

The Lass o' Carron Side

Charles James Finlayson, c. 1897

Oh! whar will I gae find a place
To close my sleepless een?
And whar will I gae seek the peace
I witless tint yestreen?
My heart that wont to dance as licht
As moonshine o'er the tide,
Now pines in thrall by luckless love
For the lass o' Carron side.

She sat the goddess of the stream
That murmured at her feet,
And aye she sang her artless sang
Wi' a voice unearthly sweet;
Sae sweet, – the birds that wont to wake
The morn wi' glee and pride,
Sat mute to hear the witching strain
O' the lass o' Carron side.

Sair may I rue my reckless haste,
Sair may I ban the hour,
That lured me frae my peacefu' cot
Within the Siren's power.
Oh! had she sprung frae humble race
As she's frae ane o' pride,
I might hae dreed a better weird
Wi' the lass o' Carron side.

First published in Harvey, William (ed. , 1897), The Harp of Stirlingshire, *J. and R. Parlane (Paisley).*

The Highlandmen Came Down the Hill

Anonymous, c. 1897

The Highlandmen came down the hill,
And owre the knowe wi' richt gude will:
Now Geordie's men may brag their fill,
For wow but they were braw, man!
They had three gen'rals o' the best,
Wi' lairds, and lords, and a' the rest,
Chiels that were bred to stand the test,
And couldna rin awa', man!

The Highlandmen are savage loons,
Wi' barkit houghs and burly crowns;
They canna stand the thunderstouns
Of heroes bred wi' care, man –
Of men that are their country's stay,
These whiggish braggarts of a day.
The Highlandmen came down the brae,
The heroes were not there, man!

Says brave Lochiel, " Pray, have we won?
I see no troop, I hear no gun."
Says Drummond, "Faith, the battle's done,
I know not how nor why, man.
But, my good lords, this thing I crave,
Have we defeat these heroes brave?"
Says Murray, " I believe we have:
If not, we're here to try, man."

But tried they up, or tried they down,
There was no foe in Falkirk town,
Nor yet in a' the country roun',
To break a sword at a', man.
They were sae bauld at break o' day,
When tow'rd the west they took their way;
But the Highlandmen came down the brae,
And made the dogs to blaw, man.

A tyke is but a tyke at best,
A coward ne'er will stand the test,
And Whigs at morn wha cocked the crest,
Or e'en had got a fa', man,
O wae befa' these northern lads,
Wi' their broadswords and white cockades!
They lend sic hard and heavy blads,
Our Whigs nae mair can craw, man.

First published in Harvey, William (ed. , 1897), The Harp of Stirlingshire, *J. and R. Parlane (Paisley), describing the Battle of Falkirk Muir, part of the Jacobite uprising of 1745. This battle was to be Bonnie Prince Charlie's last noteworthy success.*

Carronside

Mary Bowie Gillespie, c. 1897

"By the Highland hills and Lowland plains,
Through the Lothians broad and wide,
No one but Jeanie Livingstone
Will I seek to be my bride.

Oh I have lands, both gold and gear,
And my castle is right fair;
Whatever dowrie you may ha'e,
I will gi'e you ten times mair."

"Though great and fair your gold and lands
And though braw your castle be;
At hame by bonnie Carronside
I would rather wander free."

But constant rubbing wears the stone;
And the old lord in his pride
At last he took Jeanie Livingstone
To Warriston as his bride.

Her lightsome youth she left behind,
For love's altar cold and bare
Could shed no gleam of happiness
On her gold and grandeur there.

O, dowrie she gaed but the house,
And so dowie she came ben;
And she cared not for her castle fine,
For her maids and servingmen.

The tears fell on her silken seam
As it lay upon her knee;
She wept to think on Carronside –
O, were she but once more free!

Lord Warriston sat with his guests
A-drinking the red, red wine:
And first and fairest in the hall
Lady Warriston did shine.

But O, a sad heart beat beneath
Her rich robes of cramasie:
For in her lord's stern bosom reigned
The demon of jealousy.

With sparkling zone of gold and gems
Though her slender waist was spanned,
Alas! her jewelled bracelet hid
The mark of a cruel hand.

......

The screech owl cried at Warriston;
But the midnight brought no rest,
In wakeful pain the lady lay
With forebodings dire oppressed.

"What brings you here, Janet, my nurse?
O what is it you would hide?
Why come you at this hour o' nicht,
Like a ghost, to my bedside?"

The moonlight through the curtain stole
On the old crone kneeling there,
She whispered till her lady cried,
With a shudder, "Nurse, forbear!"

Next day no Warriston appeared
When the guests sat down to dine;
'Twas whispered in the company
He had taken too much wine.

They ranged themselves about the board,
Bound Warriston's vacant chair;
And none but Lady Warriston
Saw a shadow sitting there.

And O, it grew like Warriston,
She could trace each ghostly line –
She saw the marks about his neck
More livid than those of wine.

Alas! for Lady Warriston,
She sank to the floor as dead;
Alas! that Jeanie Livingstone
To the Tolbooth should be led.

The sun shone on the gruesome pile,
With its walls so strong and high,
A hapless lady knelt within,
So young, yet condemned to die.

"O Warriston, I little dreamed
The weird that we baith should dree;
I wish I ne'er had seen your face,
Or died ere you wedded me.

The sunset on my prison wall
For the last time now I see;
And never mair on Carronside
Shall I ever wander free!"

First published in Harvey, William (ed. , 1897), The Harp of Stirlingshire,
J. and R. Parlane (Paisley).

Ae' wintry nicht when winds blaw snell

John A. Thomson, 1908

Ae' Wintry nicht, when winds blew snell
A few auld cronies, and ma'sell
Forgethered, in the famous 'Star Inn'
Some cam frae Stenhousemuir and Carron
The chair wis taen, by Duncan Mac
The best o'cronies, just a crack,
He aye wi sang, the story mingles
And at his richt, sat 'Ficker Ingles',
Wha never lets the company weary
But aye appears, baith blythe and cheery,
Upon the chairman's left, I note
As guid a freend, and true a Scot
As ever wore a kilt and speuchan
I mean my auld freen Wullie Buchan
And thus he sang, in language simple
That weel-kent ballad 'Kate Dalrymple'
The rafters sang – and in the hurry
I twigged my auld freen Wullie Murray,
A' fidgin' fur tae try his haun'
At some 'auld farrant' Scottish sang
And this I dinna mean tae flatter
Weel pleased wis I when 'Afton Water'
Wis Wullie's choice tae please oor ears,
And warm oor herts and then the cheers
And lusty shouts, 'Encore! Encore!'
Wis maistly heard at Carronshore
The dram passed aften roon the table
And each ane took, whit he wis able
I noticed them that was teetotal

Paid maist attention tae the bottle
Some sing a sang, some stories tell
Some sit and listen, like masel'
Whit happened next I'm no richt shair
I somehow slipped clean aff ma chair
I maun hae been wi joy oercam'
I'm shair it couldnae be the dram,
Fun a' I had, as fawis I min'
Wis just eight nips – or wis it nine?
I widnae swear just tae a tot,
But gled I wis, when hame I got
And tae my bed, had slipped awa'
Atween the blankets bits and a'
But since that nicht I've left the bottle
And yince again, I've jined teetotal.

From notebook handwritten by John A. Thomson. Can be viewed at A1728. 001 in Falkirk Archives, Callendar House.

Amalgamation

John A. Thomson, c. 1908

While strolling through the Public Park
I there, wi Tam forgethered
He is a cheery, blythe auld spark,
And fur an oor we blethered.

We cracked on this, we cracked on that
Till wearied oot wi walkin',
We baith sat doon, and fur a while
On fitba fell a talkin'

"Weel, Tam" says I, "Whit think ye a'
This Falkirk combination?
Think ye they're better as they are,
Or wi' amalgamation?"

"I canna tell ye that," says he,
"I haena got the brains for't,
But still, its unca plain tae see
There's something wrang at Bainsford."

*From notebook handwritten by John A. Thomson. Can be viewed at A1728.
001 in Falkirk Archives, Callendar House.*

Camelon in the Shire

Corporal Dalling, c. 1916

There's a soldier lad in oor dug oot,
His name is Micky Dunn,
He keeps us aw in laughter,
For he's just a bag o' fun,
Oh he's a worthy Scotsman,
Born oh a worthy size,
For he was born in Camelon,
Dear Camelon in the Shire.

Oh every nicht aboot lichts oot,
When we lay oor blankets doon,
He clutches at wee Gibbie,
Wha's frae the same auld toon,
They wrestle for a wee while,
Then they begin to tire,
They close their een,
And dream sweet dreams
O Camelon in the Shire.

When quietness reigns in oor dug oot,
And everything's at ease
Joe Hunter cries oot
Crammies got his feet across my face,
Oh shut up Joe, Wee Wardrop cries,
Remember whaur you are
Just fecht it oot in Camelon
Dear Camelon in the Shire.

There's anither (No a Camelon lad)
Who sleeps again the door,
Yells oot enough oh Camelon,
Gie me dear auld Carronshore,
Then Rody Fraser's oot
Bull laird ye are a liar
There's no a place like Camelon
Dear Camelon in the Shire.

Wee Anderson the Drummer here
Cries oot (just for fun)
Wha ate the extra rations
They aw' yelled Micky Dunn!
Then Stalker grumbles let us sleep
And dream of them afar
Then their thochts gaun oot tae Camelon
Dear Camelon in the Shire.

There's a Stirling lad named Nisbet here
And Sneddon frae Bothkennar
Then Buchanan he's a Kelty lad
[illegible]
But when this war is ended
And the time comes tae cease fire
I hope we'll meet the gither
At Camelon in the Shire.

Manuscript handwritten by Coroporal Dalling, 2ⁿᵈ Seaforth Highlanders, describing a group of soldiers sharing Dalling's dugout during the First World War. Can be viewed at A162.001 in Falkirk Archives, Callendar House.

Redding, 25th Sept 1923

Alexander Stewart, 1923

Over the moorlands of Redding
The Michaelmass mune
In its glory an' splendor
Shone bricht – frae alune;

Wi a lustre unsullied
Its bonnie, white ray
Till doon like a mauther
Ower Wallacestone Brae

The wee ones were sleeping –
Their troubles took wing
As they dreamed of the pleasures
Tomorrow would bring

An' the silence of midnight
Encircled the land
Which the wonderful Architect
Fashioned an' planned.

There was peace on the hillside
An' naething to fear;
None knew that disaster
Was looming so near.

But just as the dawning
Grew red in the east,
The earth gave a shiver
The restfulness ceased.

For the terrible Reaper
Had suddenly come,
An' his breath upon Redding
Blew chilly an' numb.

For doon where the toilers
Were doing their bit
In the gloom of the roadways,
That wind thro' the pit

The water came rushing
Wi ominous boom,
An' the men in a moment
Were closed in a tomb.

There were deeds full of daring
That tongue canna tell,
Outcrying the heroes
Frae Sparta who fell.

An' we pray that the Highest
May soften the blow
For the friends of the victims
Who perished below,

Whose fate shall be whispered
In cottage an ha',
Long ages hereafter
In accents of awe.

Can be viewed at 941. 3187 in Falkirk Archives, Callendar House.

Fa'kirk Fe'en Fair

Anonymous, c. 1925

To the feein fair at Falkirk, Flora cam frae Stenhousemuir,
Wi' a feather in her bonnet, An' a jewel in her hair,
An' she [illegible] he callous turn aboot wi' her camisteerie air,
For she wasna' just a fawkie
at the Fa'kirk feein fair.

Comin owre the road by Carron an' this Grahamston to the fair,
Flora met some randy beggars but she gi'ed them a' a skair,
Sae the tinkers ca'd her "Cuthy-Kate", she was sae deil-ma-care
That they kend she wadna fa' a hurt
at the Fa'kirk feein fair.

When she crossed the Crooded Market, an' gaed up the Vicar Brae,
She had seekers daffin wi' her but she made them a look blae
An faed stottin' owre the [illegible]
For the trick he tried to play
She had played wi bools an' peeries
An' flown dragons in her day.

Tam, the Camelon smith can forret, but she didna toss her heid
Kim and her checked up the High Street
Like twa' bairns o' Falkirk breed
Silly cops aboot the Steeple said that Tam was past remead
An' the lass, they said had muckle on't,
But little in her heid.

At the shows they joined their cronies
Haein shies an' pitchin rings;
Turn-aboot they tried the shootin',
A'-at-aince they boarded swings;
When they mounted hobby-horses, Flora tied her strings
An' cried, "Noo Tam ye'll haud me ticht, Im feart ae pownie flings" .

Wi the babbling an' the lauchin a' the lassies sides were sair,
An' the hamegaun was as merry a' the way to Stenhousemuir
On thro' Bainsford, owre the water, mony a braw bewitchin air
Ou the concertina cheered them up the road frae Fa'kirk Fair.

This handwritten manuscript can be viewed as part of the Love Collection/ Family & Personal Papers Group at A001. 036 in the Falkirk Archives, Callendar House.

Auld Fa'kirk Toon and its Bairns

John Fleming, c. 1928

To the tune of Auld Lang Syne.

Auld Fa'kirk toon those past few years
Has greatly been improved;
Its narra' wynds and narra' lanes
Are nearly a' removed

[Chorus:]

For auld lang syne, my bairns,
For auld lang syne:
We'll hae a drink at the auld cross well
For the days o' auld lang syne.

But time brings changes tae us a';
Auld Fa'kirk's no the same:
They've improved the Auld Cow Wynd,
And changed its ancient name.

(Chorus)

They've improved the Auld Kirk Wynd,
And brocht it up to date
To suit the traffic noo-a-days,
Which flee at sic a rate.

(Chorus)

And Wast the toon, at the Croon Hotel,
There was aince a narra' lane,
But noo a fine broad street is formed –
The Lint Riggs is its name.

(Chorus)

There's room for mair improvements yet –
The East End's jist no richt;
For when a tramcar's passing by,
Ye hae tae squeeze gey ticht.

(Chorus)

The Iron Duke, wi' his black horse,
Frae the cross has slipped awa'
Tae a stand doon at Newmarket Street,
Whaur thae baith look unco braw.

(Chorus)

But still the Auld Cross Well remains,
Unmoved thro' lapse o' time;
Tae the Bairns it brings sweet memories back
O' the guid auld days lang syne.

(Chorus)

In bygone years the Steeple held
Such men as broke the laws,
And on the Steeple tap there stands
A cock that never craws.

(Chorus)

Guid luck tae a' the Fa'kirk bairns,
Aye mind "touch ane touch a'."
Ye should see them doon at Brockville Park
They're a' crazy o'er Fitba'.

(Chorus)

Noo Fa'kirk bairns, tak' my advice,
The bettin' craze aye shun,
And live an honest, righteous life,
Until yer race is run.

(Chorus)

Sae here's guid health tae Fa'kirk Bairns
At Hame and ower the seas;
We'll mind whaur Rabbie Burns slept,
Inside the Auld Cross Keys

(Chorus)

And at the wast end o' the toon
A grand auld fountain stands,
Bearing Fa'kirk's motto, we'll ne'er forget
Though traversing foreign lands.

(Chorus)

Can be viewed at A940. 003 in the Falkirk Archives, Callendar House.

An Address Tae Auld Fa'kirk Steeple

(damaged by lightning during a thunderstorm, June, 1927)

John Fleming, 1928

Oh!dear auld stately Fa'kirk Steeple
Like ivy, happy memories aroond ye cling,
I ha'e offin glanced up at yer clock,
And listened tae yer sweet familiar ring.

For years Jenny Hutton rang yer bell,
Which proclaimed the time tae great and sma',
And yer prison cells secured wi' iron bars,
Aince held the folk wha broke the law.

But Jenny has lang since passed awa'
Tae that immortal "Land o' the Leal,"
Whaur we ken there's naither grief nor pain,
And whaur the bells hae a Heavenly peel.

Mony a New Year has yer bell proclaimed the dawn
While at the Cross a'budy sang wi' glee –
"A Guid New Year tae ane an' a".
And mony a ane may ye see.

But, alas! yer unfortunate year has cam,
When the thunder rolled and the lightning flashed,
Which struck and destroyed yer ancient spire,
And doon on tae the street it crashed.

Yer grand auld clock being also damaged,
We missed the familiar soond o' yer bell;
Yet close by yer side there stood unscathed
Yer time-worn crony, the "Auld Cross Well."

If the twa o' ye could only speak,
Some strange stories I'm shair ye could tell
O' queer scenes in the High Street o' Fa'kirk,
Which re-echoed wi' the soond o' yer bell.

Whin the Fa'kirk Bairns beheld yer shattered form,
I've nae doot but their hearts were sair,
As they thocht hoo ye had firmly stood
The test o' a hundred years and mair.

A year has gane since ye met yer fate,
And still we gaze up at yer shattered form,
Which reminds us o' the year the lightning destroyed
Yer ancient spire during a thunder storm.

But yer shattered spire will be erected again,
For hoo lang nae mortal tongue can tell;
And the bairns will admire ye again wi' pride,
While listening tae the sweet soond o' yer bell.

Ring, on ring on, long may ye ring,
Yer grand auld familiar Steeple bell;
Tae the bairns happy memories like ivy clings
Aroond baith you and the "Auld Cross Well."

The Steeple was erected in 1814, and its spire was destroyed by lightning in 1927. Its time-worn crony the Auld Cross Well, was erected in 1810. This poem can be viewed at A431.002 in the Falkirk Archives, Callendar House.

Carron Glen

James Brown, 1932

Once more on Carron's banks I rove
And hear the laverock sweetly sing,
Once more I wander through the grove
Where thick the hips and hazels hing;
For there the wildflowers sweetly blaw,
Each fairy nook an' turn I ken.
So often at the evening's fa'
I muse on thee, sweet Carron Glen.

The "Lady's Loup" I ken fu' weel,
Where Carron's dark brown waters fa';
The "Hermitage" I often spiel
When oot to catch a troot or twa.
A' nature's charms are blended there,
And mony a canty'oor I spen'
When'er I ha'e the time to spare,
And muse in thee, sweet Carron Glen.

The river sings a sang fu' sweet,
It splashes, dashes, rows alang,
While frae the grove we get a treat,
The mavis floods the glen wi' sang;
The echo rings frae bank to brae
Till lost in some sweet, mossy den.
And, oh! the sacred joys I ha'e
While musing in sweet Carron Glen.

The fishes loup frae oot the stream,
And try to catch the jinkin' fly,
While thro' the trees a crimson gleam
Proclaims the evening'oor is nigh.
And then the sun, in purple drest,
Gangs sunken doon ahint yon fien;
'Tis then I lo'e to wander best,
And muse in thee, sweet Carron Glen

First published in Brown, James (1932), Songs and Poems *(John McCallum & Co, Glasgow).*

The Braw Toon o' Grangemouth

William Gordon, 1946

A braw toon, noo, is Grangemouth,
And brawer yet'twill be
Planned as a garden city,
And graced wi' flow'r and tree.
The Forth spreads fair before it
Bright under sun or moon,
Green shelt'ring hills surround it,
And kindly-like look doon.

A peacefu' place is Grangemouth,
No gangsters in't ava,
But decent-minded people,
Wi' due respect for law.
It swarms wi' bonnie lasses
And brawny men and braw,
Who'd match the lads o' Gala
Or men o' Gallowa'.

The busy port o' Grangemouth
Brings ships frae mony lands;
The docks, the works, and wood-yards
Gie work to willing hands.
But Grangemouth should be bigger,
And could be bigger soon,
If a' the men that wirk in't
Had hooses in the toon.

First published in Gordon, William (1946), Pictures in Verse, *Jamieson & Munro Ltd (Stirling).*

Go To Denny

William Gordon, 1946

I once went up the Campsie way
To spend a quiet holiday –
To smell bean-fields and new-cut hay,
And maybe save a penny.
A smart, young girl in my lodgings there
Prepared and served my daily fare;
She had rosy cheeks and golden hair,
And I fell in love with Jenny.

I gormandized on country fare –
Fresh eggs, thick cream, and butter rare,
Hare soup, and scones as light as air –
And all prepared by Jenny.
"You're just the lass for me," I said,
"I'm sure I ne'er saw sweeter maid;"
Disdainfully she tossed her head,
And said – "O, Go to Denny."

I ventured to propose a walk –
An ev'ning stroll, a quiet talk;
She curled her lip and turned her back,
And bade me "Go to Denny!"
My feelings made me force the pace,
I clasp'd her in a close embrace;
She struggled free, and slapped my face.
And hissed out –" Go to Denny."

" O, Jenny, Jenny! For me you were too many-
I thought I surely had the art
To win a country lassie's heart;
You spurned my wooing from the start,
With your "swear-phrase" – "Go to Denny."

First published in Gordon, William (1946), Pictures in Verse, *Jamieson &
Munro Ltd (Stirling).*

Author Biographies

Bethany Ruth Anderson is a Falkirk-born writer who enjoys scribbling poetry and prose. She has an MLitt in Creative Writing from Glasgow University, and her short stories and poems have been published in various places, including *From Glasgow to Saturn*, *Octavius*, *Untitled*, and Book Week Scotland's *Treasures* project. Bethany's debut novel *Swings and Roundabouts* explores relationships and mental illness, and was published in late 2013. She is continuing to work on further novels and, in the mean time, reviews books and writes about writing at www.subtlemelodrama.com.

Samuel Best's short fiction has been published in magazines in Britain, North America, and Scandinavia, and his début novel *Shop Front* was published by Fledgling Press in 2014. It tells the story of a group of small town Linlithgow boys drawn into a world of shelf-stacking, A&E visits, and knife-crime, and has been described as "an engaging, moving and fulfilling novel" and "genuinely shocking". When not writing, Best runs *Octavius*, a literary magazine based in Scotland which publishes new writing every Saturday, and can be found wasting time on Twitter at @spbbest. He grew up in and around Falkirk and now lives in Glasgow with his girlfriend and guinea pig.

Alan Bissett grew up in Hallglen, Falkirk. He is a novelist, playwright, editor and performer who now lives outside Glasgow. In 2012 he was named Glenfiddich Spirit of Scotland Writer of the Year. He has written extensively about Falkirk, most notably in his novels *Boyracers* (2001), *The Incredible Adam Spark* (2005) and *Pack Men* (2011), which was shortlisted for the Scottish Mortgage Investment Trust Fiction of the Year Prize, and his smash-hit 'one-woman show' *The Moira Monologues* (2009). The short documentary which he worked on with Adam Stafford, *The Shutdown* (2009), about the Grangemouth Oil Refinery won numerous awards at international and domestic film festivals. In 2008 he was named Falkirk Personality of the Year. His *Collected Plays* were published in February 2015.

Peter Callaghan graduated from the Royal Conservatoire of Scotland in 1998 and has worked as an actor, writer and drama workshop leader. Not to mention barman, joiner's labourer and humble measurer of the domestic brick. He has devised a number of theatre-in-education plays which continue to tour schools and community venues throughout Scotland. And is also a proud Lauriestonian!

Paul Cowan was born and grew up in Falkirk. On leaving school he trained as a welder, a line of work he is still in today. When working down in London in 2004 he was inspired to write by observing the skyline at night, society, and the various and colourful characters he worked with. This passion for writing grew as Paul worked up and down the country. Paul finally settled back in his home town in 2008. He has performed his short stories and poems at events in Falkirk and the surrounding areas. His work has been published in *Untitled* magazine and he is currently working with another local artist on the publication of his first book of poetry and short stories.

Karyn Dougan is a spoken word performer across the UK and winner of a Bookseller Bursary. This is her first official published piece. Now working as a proofreader in her home town of Falkirk, her BA Hons in English is finally being put to good use. She has also reviewed fiction for *The Skinny* and *The List* magazines. She likes to think her unhealthy addiction to Twitter makes her a better writer...

Lorna Fraser is a keen writer of fiction, with many short stories completed over the past few years. A number of her short stories have been successful in competitions, including those run by the Scottish Association of Writers. She enjoys writing contemporary stories but, as a graduate of history, it is the past that continues to fascinate and inspire her creativity. Lorna's current writing project is a novel set in the first half of the twentieth century. It will feature a Scottish-Swiss heroine and draw inspiration from some local history.

Matt Hamilton is a novelist and short story writer. His darkly comic debut novel *Strathcarnage* was published by Matador in 2009 and he is currently working on the sequel. When he's not frightening strangers and polluting the local water supply with his writing, he's fourth in command in the second biggest Post Office in the 20th most populous settlement in Scotland. You can contact him with general chat, worldly advice and offers of general psychiatric help at: strathcarnage@hotmail.com.

Gordon Legge was born in Falkirk, brought up in Grangemouth. He likes Josephine Tey and Shirley Jackson. He doesn't like author bio's. 'All She Was Worth' is from a novel in progress about a girl who died, an artist.

Helen MacKinven writes contemporary Scottish fiction, with a particular interest in exploring themes such as social class and identity, using black comedy and featuring Scots dialect. She graduated with merit from Stirling University with an MLitt in Creative Writing in 2012. Helen's short stories have appeared in a number of anthologies and literary journals, such as *Gutter* magazine and one of her novels was shortlisted in a UK-wide competition by Hookline Books. Her debut novel, *Talk of the Toun*, a coming-of-age story set in 1985 in the Falkirk area will be published by ThunderPoint in October 2015. Born in Falkirk, Helen spent her childhood and most of her adult years in Bonnybridge but now lives in North Lanarkshire. Helen blogs at helenmackinven. co. uk and you can find her on Twitter as @HelenMacKinven.

Brian McCabe was born in a small mining community near Edinburgh. In the 1950s his family moved to Falkirk and he attended Falkirk High School. He studied Philosophy and English Literature at Edinburgh University. He has lived as a freelance writer since 1980. He has held various writing fellowships, including those at Edinburgh University and the University of St Andrews and he was Editor of *Edinburgh Review* 2005-2010. Currently he is a Lecturer in Creative Writing at Lancaster University and Edinburgh University and a Royal Literary Fellow at Glasgow University. He has published three collections of poetry, the most recent being *Zero* (Polygon, 2009). He has published one novel and five collections of short stories, the most recent being *A Date With My Wife* (Canongate). His *Selected Stories* was published by Argyll.

A 45-year career has established Falkirk born **Brian McNeill** as an acclaimed force in Scottish music – as performer, composer, producer, teacher, musical director and interpreter of Scotland's past, present and future. He was described as 'Scotland's most meaningful contemporary songwriter' (*The Scotsman*) and 'The Yew Tree', 'Strong Women Rule Us All With Their Tears' and 'No Gods and Precious Few Heroes' are among songs covered worldwide. Two lines from his iconic 'Lads O' The Fair' form part of a viewpoint over his home town at the renovated Policy Bing. A voracious reader of history and all kinds of fiction, Brian's own writing includes novels – *The Busker*, *To Answer The Peacock* and... *In The Grass* – and short stories. His new novel, *No Easy Eden*, will be published soon. For six years he was Head of Scottish Music at the Royal Scottish Academy of Music and Drama. www.brianmcneill.co.uk.

Aidan Moffat, from Falkirk, has been writing and recording music since 1996, with ten years on vocals in Arab Strap, a few instrumental records as L. Pierre, an album of prose and poetry, and many collaborations. His 2011 album with Bill Wells, *Everything's Getting Older*, won the inaugural Scottish Album Of The Year Award, and his first children's book, *The Lavender Blue Dress*, was published in 2014. He's lived in Glasgow since 1999.

Gary Oberg is a native of Tamfourhill. He has spent all of his 45 years in the Falkirk district and he currently lives in Grangemouth. *Under Prospect Hill* is Gary's first published work, but he has also recently completed his first novel *Down Bromian Way* which draws extensively on his childhood experiences growing up in Falkirk. He is now currently working on a second novel. Gary attended the University of Stirling as a mature student and he graduated with a First Class Honours in English Literature, as well as achieving the Edward and Thomas Lunt award for academic excellence. He can be reached online at garyt.oberg@gmail.com.

Janet Paisley is an award-winning poet, playwright and author whose work is published internationally in numerous countries and more than a dozen languages. Her work includes 6 poetry collections, 2 historical novels, 1 novella, 2 books of short stories, plays and drama for theatre, film, radio and television, and various works for children and young people. Her most recent books are *Sang fur the Wandert, Warrior Daughter,* and *White Rose Rebel*. Janet grew up in Avonbridge, attended Falkirk High school and Callendar Park College of Education, has lived in Bothkennar, Skinflats, Standburn, and currently lives in Glen Village.

Constaince Saim-Hunter was born on March 27th 1953 in Falkirk and has five brothers and sisters. She attended Victoria Primary then Falkirk High School. In 1971 she went to Aberdeen University but decided to drop out and go to France, initially for a year. She ended up staying on for another forty one years. She met and married her French husband there and they have three children. She has lived and worked in Switzerland, Normandy, Paris, Vendee and Tunisia. She worked in various hotels then The American Hospital in Paris in administration before going back to finish her interrupted studies. She went on to teacher-training college in La Roche-sur-Yon, then worked as a Primary school teacher for 17 years, before taking early retirement. She and her husband moved to Djerba in Tunisia for a year before deciding to come back to Falkirk last October.

Lindsay Scott was born in Edinburgh, raised in Hawick in the Scottish Borders and has lived in Falkirk for the past 15 years. He has variously worked as a bank clerk, a professional musician (playing and touring with David Bowie on the 1972 Ziggy Stardust UK tour), a ship-building design draftsman in Germany during the 'Auf Wiedersehen Pet' years, a barman, a labourer, a sound engineer, a broadcast journalist with, amongst others, the BBC World Service and CNN International and the communications manager of a large charity working for and with older people. He recently joined the Falkirk Writers' Circle and this is his first serious attempt to fictionalise some of his news gathering experiences in Africa between 1980 and 2000.

Dickson Telfer lives in Falkirk and supports East Stirlingshire. He has two short fiction collections, *The Red Man Turns to Green* and *Refrigerator Cake*, with Fledgling Press, and is currently working on his first novel. He also features regularly in London-based litzine, *Push*, which is sold on the street and at football matches.

Artist, illustrator and graphic designer **Paul Tonner** won his first national literary prize in 1982 at the tender age of 11, a runner up in the Cadbury Children's Poetry Competition. Overwhelmed by this success, he decided to take a sabbatical from his glorious writing career until the year 2013, when he wrote another poem. It was deemed 'not bad' and so he continued to write things down. In early 2014 he read some of the things out to a small audience in a Falkirk café and found, surprisingly, that he was not pelted with half-eaten muffins. Encouraged by this, he continues to write stuff down and occasionally reads it out loud. He does not know how long his luck will last.

David Victor (aka Dave Trotsky) was born on the banks of Loch Lomond, briefly incarcerated in Cumbernauld, before maturing like a fine bottle of Buckie in Falkirk. David Victor is famous for designing Calley the Callendon (official Callendar Square Mascot 1992-2012), winning the DUSA Creative Writing competition 2002, faltering as a novelist, teaching poetry, plays and prose for 12 years, publishing the collaborative e-novel *The First Year of Trouble at Bannside High*, and presiding for the last five years as Grand Commissar of The Babel Zoo Writing Emporium. Writers of the world unite!

Claire Wilson is a 30 year old aspiring writer from Falkirk. Claire has dreamed of pursuing a career in Creative Writing since the age of 8. She currently moonlights as a Civil Servant by day, a position that she has held for 14 years. She has written 11 novels and over 60 short stories, all at various stages of completion and success. Claire cites Stephen King, Irvine Welsh, Richard Matheson and Val McDermid as her main influences. 95% of One Big Sunday in Falkirk may or may not be true. However, Claire has since moved on from her love of pop music to a more mature sound. Claire would like to dedicate her story to her son, Callum, and would also like to thank Denise Paterson and Carlyn Murray for their suggestions and research.

ACKNOWLEDGEMENTS

Alan Bissett and Falkirk Community Trust would like to thank the following for their hard work, enthusiasm and support in helping to bring this anthology together:

Gill Tasker and Helen Sedgwick at Cargo Publishing; the contributors; Falkirk Archives; Emma Henderson, Public Image Communications; Creative Scotland; the staff from Falkirk Community Trust Culture & Libraries service who worked on the project.

Falkirk Community Trust gratefully acknowledge the support of Falkirk Council.

Supported by
The National Lottery®
through Creative Scotland

ALBA | CHRUTHACHAIL

creative place awards
winner 2014

Falkirk
Community
Trust